A Revision Guide for the National Curriculum

Science (Double Award)
Key Stage 4

(for grades A, B, C or D)
(with the material for the higher tier examination)

Dr. Ron Joyner

Walrus Books Lt

Science: Key Stage 4 (Double Award)

Life Processes . . . Page number

Physical Processes . . . Page number

Materials . . . Page number

Physical Processes (continued) Page number

The author is grateful to Dr. Roger Norris and Chloe Joyner for their advice and help with the tedious task of checking for errors.

Walrus Books

Published by Walrus Books Ltd.

Post–Dearing edition 1997

Information about this guide and how to get the best from it.

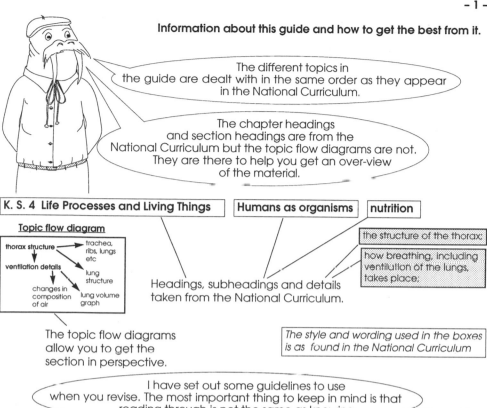

The different topics in the guide are dealt with in the same order as they appear in the National Curriculum.

The chapter headings and section headings are from the National Curriculum but the topic flow diagrams are not. They are there to help you get an over-view of the material.

K. S. 4 Life Processes and Living Things

Humans as organisms

nutrition

Topic flow diagram

thorax structure → trachea, ribs, lungs etc

ventilation details

lung structure

changes in composition of air

lung volume graph

the structure of the thorax;

how breathing, including ventilation of the lungs, takes place;

Headings, subheadings and details taken from the National Curriculum.

The topic flow diagrams allow you to get the section in perspective.

The style and wording used in the boxes is as found in the National Curriculum

I have set out some guidelines to use when you revise. The most important thing to keep in mind is that reading through is not the same as knowing.

It is unfortunate but true that revision is quite hard work. In a way it is just as well because if passing exams was that easy the certificates would have less value for us.

1. Ask your teacher to explain the bits that you don't understand, or bit which seems to be wrong (even with very careful checking, mistakes **do** get through).

2. Look up any difficult words, doing this is much better than letting them frighten you. (There is a Walrus Science Dictionary.)

3. Make sure you know the units really well. Units are worth marks in the exams (particularly at KS 4).

4. Use pen and paper to summarise the information into your own style; graphs and pictures are easier to remember than paragraphs of writing.

5. Start each work session by going over the section you last covered. A quick reminder before the information fades tends to make it stick much longer.

Questions and Answers for GCSE (ISBN 1-900290-13-8) has been written specifically to accompany this book. It is designed to check that you know the facts, as well as to extend your understanding of science.

K. S. 4 Life Processes and Living Things

Life processes and cell activity

the life processes common to plants and animals;

	Animals	Organs involved	Plants	Organs involved
Nutrition	Animals need food to supply energy, body building proteins and other substances (calcium for bone, iron, iodine and other elements for various body processes). They get all of these from their food.	Alimentary tract, liver and pancreas	Plants must have minerals from the soil. They get their energy from sunlight through photosynthesis.	Leaves and roots

Exchanging gases	Animals:
	    Take oxygen in
	        Carbon dioxide out
		Lungs and the rest of the respiratory system	Plants:
			    Take in
			    carbon dioxide
			        Oxygen out
				Leaves and stomata

Respiration	The release of energy from carbohydrates or fats using enzymes. Respiration takes place in cells. **Aerobic** respiration involves oxygen. **Anaerobic** respiration takes place when oxygen is not present.	Cells, cytoplasm and mito-chondria	Much as happens in animal cells except that anaerobic respiration in animals produces lactic acid, In plants ethanol is produced.	Cells, cytoplasm and mito-chondria
Removal of body waste (excretion)	A liquid waste is produced. This contains a poisonous substance (urea) released when amino acids are broken down in the body. Carbon dioxide from the lungs as is bile from the liver.	The kidneys, lungs, liver and skin	Plants produce oxygen as a waste product when it is sunny. Other waste molecules are stored in bark, dying leaves, old wood and cell vacuoles.	Oxygen leaves through the stomata
Responses	Many animals need to respond quite rapidly to threats or changes in their surroundings.	Organs of the nervous system and muscles	Plants are capable of only gradual responses like growing towards the light, roots growing downwards.	No organs involved
Movement	Vertebrates use pairs of muscles working together with bones to produce movement.			
Growth	During growth the organism increases in size. This increase takes place because cells divide and then get larger.		As with animals, plants grow because their cells divide and enlarge.	
Reproduction	Only those organisms that make reproduction their main concern in life will continue to survive. An organism that does not pass its genes on to the next generation effectively becomes extinct. This is true for both plants and animals.			
		Ovaries, testes etc. (see p 36)		Ovaries, stamens etc. (p 37)

Cells | Cells are tiny pieces of living material surrounded by a membrane (membrane and cell wall in plants). The membrane gives cells control over their internal environment. Without membranes there cannot be life.

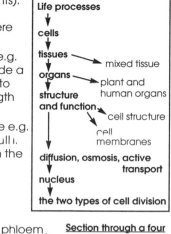

Life processes
↓
cells
↓
tissues → mixed tissue
↓
organs → plant and
structure   human organs
and function
↓   cell structure
        cell
        membranes
diffusion, osmosis, active
        transport
nucleus
↓
the two types of cell division

Tissues | Tissues are groups of cells that work together e.g. in xylem tissue, the cells act together to provide a system of tubes for water transport from roots to the rest of the plant (they may also add strength to the stem).

Simple tissue. All the cells are of the same type e.g. the epithelium that lines the inside of your mouth.

Three examples of mixed plant tissue

Mixed tissue. Different cells may be present in the tissue as occurs in blood, bone, muscle or the woody tissue of plants.

Phloem
1 The cells contain living cytoplasm.
2 Each conducting cell has a companion cell beside it.
3 The cells actively move sugars, amino acids, organic acids and other molecules, around the plant.

phloem
cambium
xylem

Section through a four year old woody stem

Xylem
1. When the xylem cells are mature, they contain no cytoplasm., i.e. they are dead cells.
2. The end walls where the cells joined originally have disappeared so that very long tubes are formed.
3. They have thickened walls to withstand the pressures from the outside caused by tension in the long thread of water from root to leaf. This tension might otherwise cause them to collapse.
4. They conduct water and minerals (as ions) from the roots to the leaves.

Cambium | The cambium is a layer of cells found between xylem and phloem. Because these cells are constantly dividing, they keep making new phloem and xylem for the plant.

that organ systems are adapted for their roles in life processes:

Organs | Organs are composed of at least two types of tissue which work together. For example, the heart is made of muscle, fibrous tissue, blood vessels and nerves all working together to pump blood.

Organs in plants | The term organ is not a precise one, the alimentary tract is an organ but so is the stomach, large intestine etc.

— Flowers: sexual reproduction takes place here

— Leaves: they contain the light–collecting cells in which energy is used to make glucose from carbon dioxide and water. The cells are arranged to promote gas exchange with the outside

— Stem: water and dissolved minerals from the soil move up special tubes (vessels) in the stem. Sugars and other chemicals move up and down through living cells in the outer part of the stem. Stems also keep the plant upright, exposing the leaves to the sun etc.

— Roots: they have a very large surface area for absorbing water and minerals from around soil grains. The absorbing surfaces have a covering of root hairs each made from a single cell. Roots can be selective to some extent, in what minerals they absorb from the soil

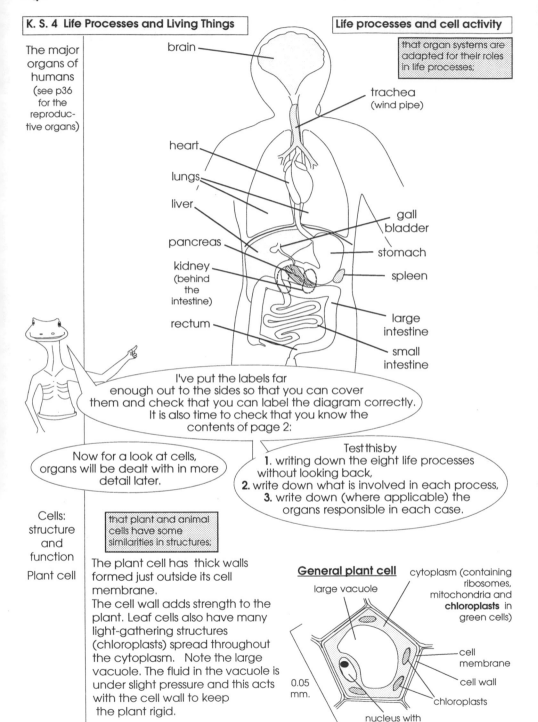

K. S. 4 Life Processes and Living Things

Life processes and cell activity

The major organs of humans (see p36 for the reproductive organs)

that organ systems are adapted for their roles in life processes;

brain

trachea (wind pipe)

heart

lungs

liver

gall bladder

pancreas

stomach

kidney (behind the intestine)

spleen

rectum

large intestine

small intestine

I've put the labels far enough out to the sides so that you can cover them and check that you can label the diagram correctly. It is also time to check that you know the contents of page 2:

Now for a look at cells, organs will be dealt with in more detail later.

Test this by
1. writing down the eight life processes without looking back,
2. write down what is involved in each process,
3. write down (where applicable) the organs responsible in each case.

Cells: structure and function

that plant and animal cells have some similarities in structures;

Plant cell

The plant cell has thick walls formed just outside its cell membrane.
The cell wall adds strength to the plant. Leaf cells also have many light-gathering structures (chloroplasts) spread throughout the cytoplasm.   Note the large vacuole. The fluid in the vacuole is under slight pressure and this acts with the cell wall to keep the plant rigid.

General plant cell

cytoplasm (containing ribosomes, mitochondria and **chloroplasts** in green cells)

large vacuole

cell membrane

cell wall

chloroplasts

0.05 mm.

nucleus with nucleolus

Animal cell

cytoplasm (containing mitochondria, a system of membranes and more)

Two views of a general animal cell

cell membranes

nucleus with nucleolus

By all means draw a fried egg for a simple animal cell but at GCSE level you are expected to show that you know that cytoplasm is much more complicated than egg white and the nucleus is more complicated than cooked yolk.

The main differences between plant and animal cells

Plant Cells	Animal Cells
Cell wall with a membrane inside it.	They have a cell membrane but no cell wall.
Cytoplasm contains large vacuoles.	Cytoplasm may have many, very small, vacuoles (called vesicles).
Chloroplasts are usually present (in leaf and some stem cells).	There are no chloroplasts, and . . .
Cytoplasm may be seen to be moving around the cell (streaming).	There is no cytoplasmic streaming.
Most plant cells are much larger than animal cells.	Most are much smaller than plant cells (ten times or so).

Structure is linked to the task performed by the cell (four examples from animal tissue)

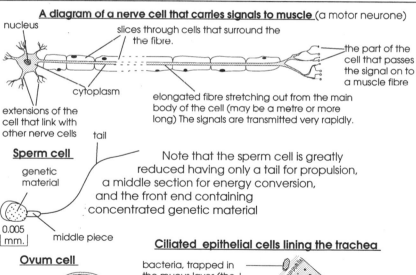

A diagram of a nerve cell that carries signals to muscle (a motor neurone)

nucleus

slices through cells that surround the the fibre.

the part of the cell that passes the signal on to a muscle fibre

cytoplasm

elongated fibre stretching out from the main body of the cell (may be a metre or more long) The signals are transmitted very rapidly.

extensions of the cell that link with other nerve cells

Sperm cell

tail

genetic material

Note that the sperm cell is greatly reduced having only a tail for propulsion, a middle section for energy conversion, and the front end containing concentrated genetic material

0.005 mm.

middle piece

Ovum cell

the set of chromosomes that will combine with the male chromosomes

cell membrane

cytoplasm packed with food material which will sustain the developing embryo

Ciliated epithelial cells lining the trachea

bacteria, trapped in the mucus layer (the mucus is secreted by goblet cells, which are not shown)

nuclei. They are not different sizes, its just that two are cut through the middle, the other was sliced along an edge when the section was prepared.

cilia, moving the mucus steadily towards the nose

K. S. 4 Life Processes and Living Things | **Life processes and cell activity**

<u>**Root hair cell**</u>

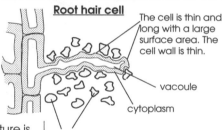

The cell is thin and long with a large surface area. The cell wall is thin.

vacoule

cytoplasm

Structure is linked to the task performed by the cell (three examples from plant tissue)

soil grains and bits of humus surrounded with a thin film of water. The hairlike extensions form a close contact with the soil particles.

Three palisade cells in part of a leaf

upper epidermal cells (no chloroplasts)

palisade cells

These cells are arranged so that they absorb the maximum amount of light. They are packed with chloroplasts.

<u>**A cross section of a stem showing xylem vessels**</u>

(see page 3 for a stem section)

living cells close to the xylem vessels.

Each cell has a nucleus but the section may be from above or below that part of the cell.

30 μm

two xylem vessels

A diagram showing that the xylem vessels extend up and down the stem

These are made from elongated cells which have grown end to end. As the cells mature the walls are strengthened. The end walls disappear and the cells then die, leaving strong walled tubes. Water can then move along the tubes from roots to the rest of the plant.

Xylem vessels are the tubes along which water and dissolved salts travel from roots to the rest of the plant.

how substances enter and leave cells through the cell membrane by diffusion, osmosis and active transport.

For our purposes today it is enough to consider what makes a cell alive.

A living cell is able to adjust concentrations of salts and other substances within itself so that these remain fairly constant even though the concentrations outside are very different and may keep changing.

The cell membrane is the controlling barrier between cytoplasm and the outside so we will have a look at it.

Cell membrane

<u>**A simple diagram showing the arrangement in a short length of cell membrane**</u>

Fatty molecules forming the main part of the membrane. As water does not get past fat easily it acts as a barrier for water and substances that dissolve readily in water.

Protein molecules in the membrane pores. These molecules use energy to move substances in or out of the cell i.e. by active transport.

Diffusion

Diffusion is the process by which particles of matter spread out into the space that is available to them. For example, if a grain of sugar is put into some water there will, at first, be a high concentration of sugar particles around the grain but as time passes all the water will become equally sweet. This change is due to diffusion.

Many substances are not able to diffuse across the cell membrane i.e. it acts as a barrier to diffusion for these substances (it is partially permeable). This is important because the cell membrane needs to separate the cytoplasm (with its high concentrations of dissolved substances) from the outside. Small molecules like water, carbon dioxide and oxygen diffuse across cell membranes. (see also page 53)

Osmosis

Osmosis is a special kind of diffusion. It occurs when there is an overall movement of water particles away from regions where water particles are very concentrated (across a partially permeable membrane). This means that water will move across a semi-permeable membrane from dilute solutions to more concentrated solutions (of salt or sugar).

Active transport

During active transport, ions or molecules will be moved across the membrane into regions of higher concentration. This needs energy (usually in the form of ATP). Proteins, embedded in membranes, are able to change their shape and so move substances from one side of the membrane to the other.

that the nucleus contains chromosomes that carry the genes;

I've set out some information on the nucleus, chromosomes and genes on this page.

A membrane containing pores separates the nuclear contents from the cytoplasm (bacteria and blue green algae do not have this membrane).

The nucleus is a region in cells that is rich in genetic material. The genetic material is found in thread-like structures which become easier to see during cell division.

1. Chromosomes occur in the nuclei of the cells of plants and animals.
2. Chromosomes contain two types of substance; deoxyribonucleic acid (DNA) and protein. The DNA carries the genetic information.
3. There are thousands of genes in every chromosome. Each gene is just a short stretch of a long-chain molecule (DNA) present in the chromosome.
4. The chromosomes occur as double sets, (e.g. human cells have 46 chromosomes, two sets of 23).
5. When sex cells (eggs, sperm, etc) are formed during meiosis, each sex cell gets only one set, i.e. human sex cells will have 23 chromosomes each.

A diagram showing a single chromosome

centromere

chromatids

The chromatids contain coiled threads of the chemical (DNA) that carry the genetic information. The threads of DNA are tightly coiled and combined with protein.

K. S. 4 Life Processes and Living Things

Mitosis
(the cells produced are identical to the parent cell)

Mitosis produces cells that are genetically identical to the parent cells. There is no halving of the chromosome number.

A diagram showing the main stages of mitosis

prophase

This cell is about to divide. The nucleus is visible but no chromosomes can be seen yet.

Division has begun, the nuclear membrane has disappeared and thread-like chromosomes are now seen.

metaphase

The chromosomes are seen to be made of pairs of identical threads (the chromatids).

anaphase

In the next stage the chromatids pull apart.

telophase

Membranes (and cell walls in plant cells) form between the new cells.

Meiosis
(halves the chromosome number; produces gametes)

To keep it simple, we will imagine a cell with only **one pair** of chromosomes (human cells have 23 pairs)

A diagram showing the main stages of meiosis

1. This cell is about to divide. The nucleus is visible but no chromosomes can be seen.

2. The chromosomes shorten and become visible. We show only one of the pairs.

3. The chromosomes pair up on the equator of the spindle.

This description only covers what can be seen down a microscope.

4. We can now see that each chromosome is a two--stranded structure. Thus each homologous pair is made of 4 strands.

5. The strands break in places and rejoin across the chromosomes.

6. They are pulled apart by spindle fibres.

7. Single chromosomes have now moved apart. The genetic information has been split between the two daughter cells.

8. Before the two daughter cells can form two new cells, a second division starts, at right angles to the first.

9. Four cells have resulted from the whole process. Each cell contains only half of the genetic information and can now form an egg, pollen grain or sperm.

These cells now only contain one of each pair of chromosomes.

A good way to get to grips with this is to make up two pairs of homologous chromosomes from string and then use these to model meiosis

To get the most benefit from this summary page,
have a go at learning it, copy down the left hand column, then close the guide
and make your own copy of the details from memory.

A summary of
the main functions of different parts of the cell

nucleus	This is where most of the genetic material is kept. Small molecules (e.g. hormones) diffuse from cytoplasm into the nucleus switching genes on or off. The nucleus holds the recipe for the proteins needed by the cell itself and by the organism.
cytoplasm	This is where most proteins and other substances are synthesised. The cytoplasm is also the place where cell respiration occurs.
cell membrane	The cell membrane acts as a barrier between much of the cytoplasm and the fluid outside the cell. It is able to use energy to pump substances into and out of the cytoplasm taking account of the needs of the cell.
cell wall	In woody plants like trees or the stems of shrubs, the cell walls are greatly thickened so that, when many cells are packed together (forming wood), they are able to support the plant. Smaller plants keep their tissues firm because water is absorbed by the cells. The cells swell until the maximum size is reached (the cell walls will not allow further expansion). The pressure inside the cells now makes the plants rigid. While there is plenty of water these plants will remain rigid otherwise they wilt.
chloroplasts	Chloroplasts contain the substances (e.g. chlorophylls), that are needed for photosynthesis. These substances are packed so that maximum light will be absorbed.
mitochondria	These are small and scattered through the cytoplasm. They contain the enzymes that transfer energy from small molecules to form ATP. Mitochondria have their own DNA and are believed to have originated when bacteria invaded nucleated cells.
endoplasmic reticulum (in higher organisms)	A system of membranes found in the cytoplasm. They can form channels in the cytoplasm keeping different parts of it separate from each other. Proteins are synthesised on endoplasmic reticulum covered with ribosomes.
ribosomes	These are tiny granules of RNA and protein that are involved in the synthesis of proteins.

Protein synthesis

cytoplasm

Most of the genes are kept in the nucleus but protein is made in the cytoplasm and so a mobile copy of the gene for that protein must exist.

nucleus

Proteins are essential for living organisms and cells have to have a reliable way of making them.

genes in the nucleus → diffusible copy of a gene (messenger RNA) → place where the protein is made (ribosomes) → protein

more detail on page 10

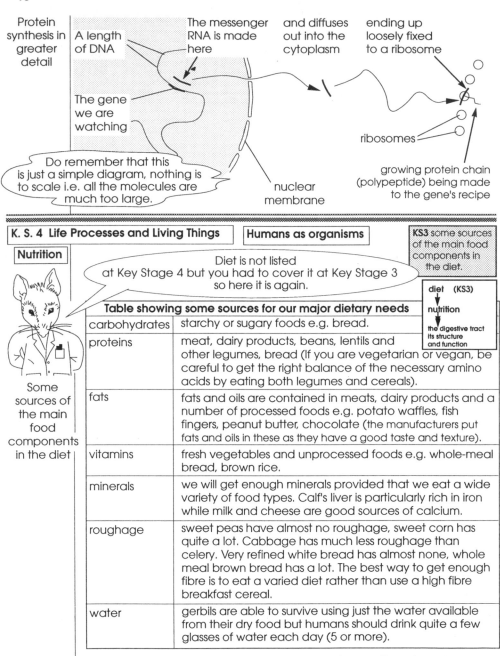

Protein synthesis in greater detail

A length of DNA

The gene we are watching

The messenger RNA is made here

and diffuses out into the cytoplasm

ending up loosely fixed to a ribosome

ribosomes

growing protein chain (polypeptide) being made to the gene's recipe

nuclear membrane

Do remember that this is just a simple diagram, nothing is to scale i.e. all the molecules are much too large.

K. S. 4 Life Processes and Living Things   **Humans as organisms**

KS3 some sources of the main food components in the diet.

Nutrition

Diet is not listed at Key Stage 4 but you had to cover it at Key Stage 3 so here it is again.

diet   (KS3)
↓
nutrition
↓
the digestive tract
its structure
and function

Some sources of the main food components in the diet

Table showing some sources for our major dietary needs	
carbohydrates	starchy or sugary foods e.g. bread.
proteins	meat, dairy products, beans, lentils and other legumes, bread (If you are vegetarian or vegan, be careful to get the right balance of the necessary amino acids by eating both legumes and cereals).
fats	fats and oils are contained in meats, dairy products and a number of processed foods e.g. potato waffles, fish fingers, peanut butter, chocolate (the manufacturers put fats and oils in these as they have a good taste and texture).
vitamins	fresh vegetables and unprocessed foods e.g. whole-meal bread, brown rice.
minerals	we will get enough minerals provided that we eat a wide variety of food types. Calf's liver is particularly rich in iron while milk and cheese are good sources of calcium.
roughage	sweet peas have almost no roughage, sweet corn has quite a lot. Cabbage has much less roughage than celery. Very refined white bread has almost none, whole meal brown bread has a lot. The best way to get enough fibre is to eat a varied diet rather than use a high fibre breakfast cereal.
water	gerbils are able to survive using just the water available from their dry food but humans should drink quite a few glasses of water each day (5 or more).

Why eat?

Food is used as a fuel during **activity** as well as for **growth and repair**.
Fuel is used to enable the beating of the heart, peristaltic waves along the intestine and ureter and movement.
For most of us, eating is a pleasant activity and not eating for a while causes discomfort. If this were not so, we would starve because we would not bother to eat.

Components in food and storage of the products of digestion

Carbohydrates Storage	These are very useful as an energy supply (mainly because small carbohydrate molecules are water-soluble and can be carried dissolved in the blood). Stored as starch (in plants) or glycogen (in animals) for future use. They are very important in plant cell walls as cellulose.
Proteins Storage	Used to help make structural elements such as ligaments, tendons and bone, movement proteins such as muscle and enzymes. Proteins have many other functions: certain hormones are very small proteins (e.g. insulin), as are the clotting substances in blood. Our bodies are unable to store excess amino acids. The amine part is changed to urea and excreted. The remainder is stored as fat or carbohydrate.
Fats (lipids) Storage	These form a very important part of the membranes which are found surrounding the cells and throughout their cytoplasm. They are used as a low-density energy store (easier to carry than sugars, but the energy in them is not as readily available as the energy from sugars). They are used, under the skin, as heat insulators, especially in aquatic mammals and in humans.
Vitamins Storage	These substances are only required in very small quantities, but they are essential for health. If they are missing from the diet, animals can suffer from 'deficiency diseases'. Vitamin C (ascorbic acid), found in vegetables and citrus fruits, is water-soluble and is essential in the synthesis of collagen (a fibrous protein found in skin and ligaments). Without it, the skin of the gums becomes weak and bleeds, wounds fail to heal and, eventually, animals would become anaemic and suffer heart failure. Vitamins A, D, E, and K are oil-soluble. It is possible for us to poison ourselves by having too much of them. Being oil soluble, they dissolve in our body fats and their concentration can rise to dangerous levels.
Fibre	The fibrous, indigestible part of food that helps the intestine to shift the food mass along. Roughage is also believed to absorb onto it's surface many of the harmful substances produced by bacteria in our intestines (nitrates, nitrites, nitrosamines) and, by doing this, reduces the risk to ourselves of getting intestinal cancers.
Minerals	Iron (Fe) Needed as part of the oxygen-carrying haemoglobin of blood; without it, some enzymes will not work. Although it is not part of the chlorophyll molecule in plants, it is needed during the synthesis of this molecule.
Water	Most of us need more water each day than we bother to drink. We do get a fair amount of water even in what looks like fairly dry food e.g. curry and rice may contain as much as 50% water. We should all drink 5 or more glasses of water each day. The really nice thing about atoms is that they can be used over and over again. They never wear out! The atoms in our bodies have been in other bodies before, some of them just a few days ago !
Mechanical breakdown of food	Our teeth, working together with the tongue, break the food up into smaller particles so that enzymes have a larger surface area to work on. This breaking up is continued by the muscular churning in the intestine.
Chemical breakdown	Digestive enzymes break bonds so that molecules separate into smaller particles.

KS3 that balanced diets contain carbohydrates, proteins, fats, minerals, vitamins and water.

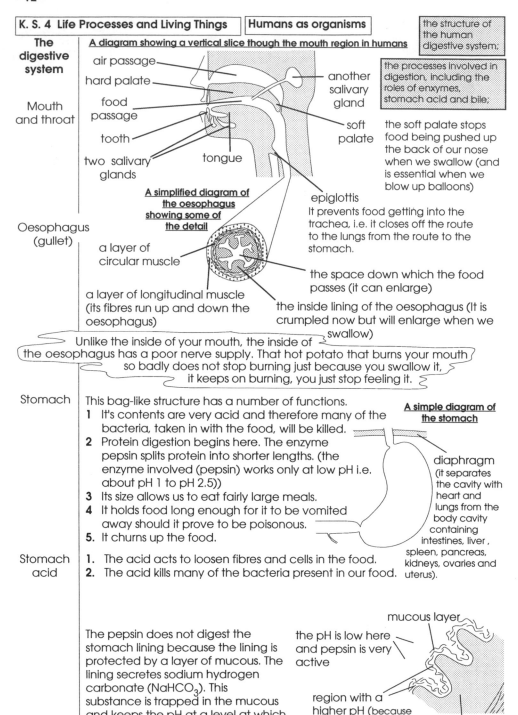

| K. S. 4 Life Processes and Living Things | Humans as organisms | the structure of the human digestive system; |

The digestive system

A diagram showing a vertical slice though the mouth region in humans

the processes involved in digestion, including the roles of enzymes, stomach acid and bile;

Mouth and throat

air passage

hard palate

food passage

tooth

two salivary glands

tongue

another salivary gland

soft palate

the soft palate stops food being pushed up the back of our nose when we swallow (and is essential when we blow up balloons)

Oesophagus (gullet)

A simplified diagram of the oesophagus showing some of the detail

a layer of circular muscle

a layer of longitudinal muscle (its fibres run up and down the oesophagus)

epiglottis
It prevents food getting into the trachea, i.e. it closes off the route to the lungs from the route to the stomach.

the space down which the food passes (it can enlarge)

the inside lining of the oesophagus (It is crumpled now but will enlarge when we swallow)

Unlike the inside of your mouth, the inside of the oesophagus has a poor nerve supply. That hot potato that burns your mouth so badly does not stop burning just because you swallow it, it keeps on burning, you just stop feeling it.

Stomach

This bag-like structure has a number of functions.
1 It's contents are very acid and therefore many of the bacteria, taken in with the food, will be killed.
2 Protein digestion begins here. The enzyme pepsin splits protein into shorter lengths. (the enzyme involved (pepsin) works only at low pH i.e. about pH 1 to pH 2.5))
3 Its size allows us to eat fairly large meals.
4 It holds food long enough for it to be vomited away should it prove to be poisonous.
5. It churns up the food.

A simple diagram of the stomach

diaphragm (it separates the cavity with heart and lungs from the body cavity containing intestines, liver, spleen, pancreas, kidneys, ovaries and uterus).

Stomach acid

1. The acid acts to loosen fibres and cells in the food.
2. The acid kills many of the bacteria present in our food.

The pepsin does not digest the stomach lining because the lining is protected by a layer of mucous. The lining secretes sodium hydrogen carbonate ($NaHCO_3$). This substance is trapped in the mucous and keeps the pH at a level at which pepsin does not remain active.

mucous layer

the pH is low here and pepsin is very active

region with a higher pH (because of the $NaHCO_4$)

stomach wall

The liver in action	The liver is the largest organ in the body. It has many functions, some of which relate to digestion. All digested food is carried by the blood stream so that it passes first through the liver before it reaches any other part of the body. The liver is able therefore to remove poisonous substances that were taken in with the food before they can do damage.

A diagram showing the stomach, small intestine and liver and the blood vessels. All blood draining the intestine must pass through the liver.

- diaphragm
- gall bladder and bile duct
- veins draining the intestine
- liver
- stomach
- pancreas
- small intestine

Bile	The liver produces bile. This is stored in the gall bladder, and then released down the bile duct into the small intestine when required after a meal. Bile contains substances that break down fats to small droplets so that enzymes are able to digest them. It also contains substances produced when red blood cells are broken down in the liver (these are excreted with the bile). Bile is alkaline; it contains sodium hydrogen carbonate ($NaHCO_3$).
Duodenum and ileum	Most digestion and absorption of food takes place in the small intestine (duodenum and ileum). Enzymes are released from the intestine wall and from the pancreas (which empties into the duodenum). Because of the villi all over the surface, there is a huge area through which digested food can diffuse or be absorbed.

A small part of the intestine wall

Villi which are well supplied with blood vessels and lymph ducts

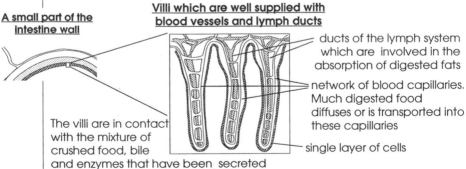

- ducts of the lymph system which are involved in the absorption of digested fats
- network of blood capillaries. Much digested food diffuses or is transported into these capillaries
- single layer of cells

The villi are in contact with the mixture of crushed food, bile and enzymes that have been secreted from the intestine wall and from the pancreas.

pH changes down the intestine	Sodium bicarbonate ($NaHCO_3$) is also released from the pancreas and from the liver (down the bile duct) and neutralises the acid that has arrived from the stomach. This is important, in the stomach the pH needs to be low because pepsin works at low pH. The enzymes in the small intestine work best at neutral pH.

A diagram showing the main organs involved in digestion

The lining on the inside of the intestine is in contact with quite damaging fluids and so is being constantly replaced. The lining is renewed every one to two days.

body cavity in which the intestines, liver, kidneys etc. are found. (referred to as the peritoneal cavity)

The colon and rectum

The colon differs from the small intestine in some important regards:
1. It has a much larger diameter.
2. There are no villi.

rectum; faeces are stored here.

colon
The surface is puckered because of the way the muscles are arranged in the colon wall. Absorption of water occurs here.

Time taken by food to get from one end to the other.

On average a meal takes about 6 hours to get from mouth to the colon. It takes a further 6 hours to reach the end of the colon. It may then take up to three days for all residues to be expelled. One way to find your own transit time is to have a large meal of corn on the cob. The seed coatings are often still visible after passing through the digestive tract. (I know it is a bit revolting but it is a useful test all the same)

Egestion

Egestion is the word used for the expulsion of faeces from the body. (Do learn the difference between this term and excretion e.g. excretion of urea by the kidneys or excretion of carbon dioxide by the lungs)

the structure of the human circulatory system, including the composition and functions of the blood;

Humans as organisms | **circulation**

A diagram showing the main vessels leaving and entering the heart

Heart

Topic flow diagram

heart structure → heart detail
circulation details
blood functions → arteries, capillaries, veins
blood: the liquid → healing of wounds
blood cells
capillaries at work

dorsal aorta (it carries blood to all parts of the body except the lungs)

Vena cavae (the large veins that drain all parts of the head and body but not the lungs and heart)

pulmonary arteries (they carry blood to the lungs)

pulmonary veins (they return blood from the lungs)

the system of veins (that help to drain the heart muscle)

coronary arteries (they supply the heart muscle) They start at the base of the dorsal aorta and take about 4% of the total heart output)

Some details about the heart

Beating rates: This varies from 50 to 100 beats per minute at rest, but the averages are 84 beats per minute for adult females and 78 beats per minute for adult males. Heartbeat can climb to 200 per minute during very vigorous exercise.

Flow rates: 170 cm^3 per beat at rest to 300cm^3+ per beat during exercise.

The heart does not empty when fully contracted. About 230 cm^3 remains in the heart even at the height of contraction.

Contractions: The nerve signal starts in the right atrium and spreads quickly to the left atrium. While these are contracting, forcing blood into the ventricles, the signal spreads slowly down to the ventricles which then contract.

More details about the heart

The main sounds of the heart beat are made when the valves snap shut at the different parts of the cycle.

Getting fit: Muscles which are made to work hard will run short of oxygen (i.e. they suffer oxygen debt, and lactic acid will build up). Lower levels of oxygen stimulate the proliferation of capillaries and so, from then on, the muscle is able to work harder i.e. it is fitter! This applies to heart muscle as well as to other body muscles.

As you get fitter your heart rate will return to normal more quickly. When you are very fit it will be back at your normal rate in 2 minutes.

Hardening of arteries: Hardening of the arteries (**atherosclerosis**) is a thickening and hardening of the walls of arteries. This is a problem because arteries need to give a little each time the ventricles contract (in this way they help to even out the pressure surge). The hardening and the fatty deposits have several effects: **1.** poor circulation because of the narrow channel, **2.** a tendency for blood to stick to the vessel walls and grow into clots (these can then block the artery further down so starving the muscle of oxygen), **3.** a tendency for the large vessels to bleed because they are no longer as stretchy (yes! large vessels have their own blood supply).

A **coronary** occurs because the arteries supplying the heart muscle have become constricted or blocked. The poor old heart has no choice but to keep on beating without the energy and oxygen supply needed for this. The severity of an attack depends on which muscles or nerves have been starved of blood (i.e. energy and oxygen), and for how long.

This is a good time to check whether you really know about the heart (rather than just think you do because you have read your school notes and the last page here)

Reading is not the same as knowing.

More parts of the heart

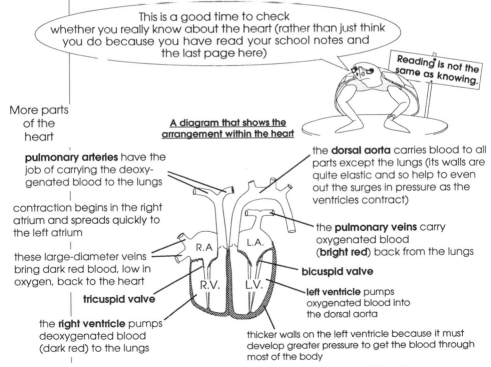

A diagram that shows the arrangement within the heart

pulmonary arteries have the job of carrying the deoxy- genated blood to the lungs

contraction begins in the right atrium and spreads quickly to the left atrium

these large-diameter veins bring dark red blood, low in oxygen, back to the heart

tricuspid valve

the **right ventricle** pumps deoxygenated blood (dark red) to the lungs

R.A   L.A.

R.V.   L.V.

the **dorsal aorta** carries blood to all parts except the lungs (its walls are quite elastic and so help to even out the surges in pressure as the ventricles contract)

the **pulmonary veins** carry oxygenated blood (**bright red**) back from the lungs

bicuspid valve

left ventricle pumps oxygenated blood into the dorsal aorta

thicker walls on the left ventricle because it must develop greater pressure to get the blood through most of the body

Important: both ventricles pump the same volume of blood at each beat. This has to be so! Assume that the volumes differed by only 0.01% per beat then after 15 minutes one side would have about 10% more blood than the other.

Humans as organisms	circulation

The parts of the circulation system

In humans, and other mammals, the heart pumps blood through two sets of vessels. One set supplies the lungs. The second set supplies all parts of the head and body.

The blood has a number of vital functions:

1. It transports digested food from the intestine to all parts of the body as small molecules in solution.

2. It transports oxygen (in the red blood cells) from the lungs to the tissues, and transports carbon dioxide (mainly in the plasma) back to the lungs. The oxygen is transported as oxyhaemoglobin. The carbon dioxide is carried mainly as hydrogen carbonate ions (HCO_3^-).

3. It transports waste products (urea, broken down hormones etc.) to the kidneys for excretion.

4. It acts to defend the body from the effects of bacterial and viral infections, and from foreign proteins in the system (the allergic response).

5. It seals wounds with a network of fibres (clots), which shrink as they dry (platelets are involved in this).

6. It plays an important part in regulating the body's temperature.

7. It plays a vital role in carrying hormones around. These are responsible for the regulation of growth rate, body temperature, reproduction, and ability to handle stress.

More on wound healing (5 above)

Things that must happen:

1. the blood loss must be stemmed;

the platelets disrupt and release substances which promote the formation of fibres in the wound

2. infection must be prevented;

the close mesh of fibres reduces the chance that bacteria are able to enter the wound

3. the wound should be closed if possible;

the fibres stick to the edges of the wound and draw them together as they dry

4. repair must begin and debris must be removed.

cells are able to migrate into the area of the wound, removing damaged tissue, laying down longer lasting fibres (collagen fibres), and remaining there to form the new tissue

blood capillaries grow into the area of the wound

It would never do for the blood to clot at the wrong time (after all clots are what cause heart attacks and some kinds of stroke) and so blood only clots in the presence of air or of damaged tissue.

Important differences between arteries, capillaries and veins

Arteries	Capillaries	Veins
Have thick elastic walls.	Walls are only one cell thick and they contain no fibres.	They have thin but strong walls that are not very elastic.
Have a regular circular shape when seen in cross-section.	Are very narrow, often only the width of a red blood cell. Walls are leaky and allow glucose, amino acids ,and other molecules through,	They appear flattened in cross-section.
Have no valves except at the heart itself.		Valves are spaced regularly along the length of the vein and act together with nearby muscles to move the blood back to the heart.
They carry blood away from the heart. Not all arteries carry oxygen-rich blood.	They carry blood between arteries and veins.	
Blood flows quickly through them, and it flows in surges.	Blood flows quite slowly and fairly smoothly; there is time enough for diffusion of substances into and out of the blood.	They carry blood back to the heart. Not all veins carry de-oxygenated blood.
		Blood flows fairly quickly and smoothly.

Composition of mammalian blood

Whole blood that has been spun for 10 minutes to separate the main components

plasma (a solution of salts, proteins, hormones and other substances making up 54% of the blood)

white blood cells and platelets make up about 1% of the blood volume

red blood cells (erythrocytes) which make up about 45% of the blood volume

blood platelets

platelets are cell fragments that can release the substances that bring about clotting

Blood cells

erythrocyte

granulocyte

lymphocyte

7.5 μm

one view of an erythrocyte showing the thinner central area

12 μm

granulocytes engulf and destroy bacteria and other invaders. They can sense the chemicals released by bacteria from a distance and then move closer to kill them.

8 μm

lymphocytes produce antibodies.

The exchange of substances at the capillaries

A diagram showing the main features of capillary bed

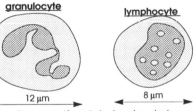

venule carrying blood back to the heart

tissue

tissue

tissue

arteriole carrying blood towards the tissue

blood pressure is higher on arteriole side so that fluid is forced out into the tissue

fluid is forced out of the vessels and mixes with fluid around the cells. Glucose, oxygen and other molecules are absorbed by the cells, waste products are released by cells.

blood pressure is lower on the venule side so that fluid flows back into the vessel (blood proteins do not leave the capillaries and are important in helping to draw fluid back into the blood system)

Humans as organisms | **breathing**

the structure of the thorax;

how breathing, including ventilation of the lungs, takes place;

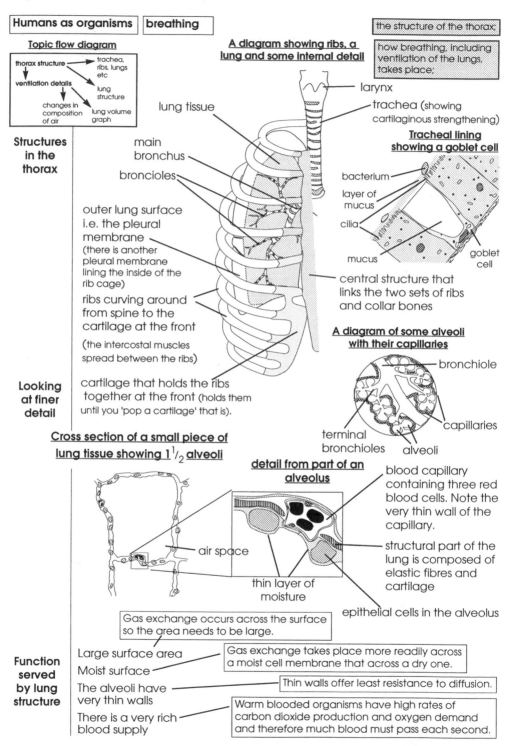

Topic flow diagram

thorax structure → trachea, ribs, lungs etc

ventilation details

lung structure

changes in composition of air

lung volume graph

A diagram showing ribs, a lung and some internal detail

larynx

trachea (showing cartilaginous strengthening)

lung tissue

main bronchus

broncioles

outer lung surface i.e. the pleural membrane (there is another pleural membrane lining the inside of the rib cage)

ribs curving around from spine to the cartilage at the front

(the intercostal muscles spread between the ribs)

cartilage that holds the ribs together at the front (holds them until you 'pop a cartilage' that is).

central structure that links the two sets of ribs and collar bones

Tracheal lining showing a goblet cell

bacterium

layer of mucus

cilia

mucus

goblet cell

A diagram of some alveoli with their capillaries

bronchiole

capillaries

terminal bronchioles

alveoli

Structures in the thorax

Looking at finer detail

Cross section of a small piece of lung tissue showing 1 1/2 alveoli

air space

detail from part of an alveolus

thin layer of moisture

blood capillary containing three red blood cells. Note the very thin wall of the capillary.

structural part of the lung is composed of elastic fibres and cartilage

epithelial cells in the alveolus

Function served by lung structure

Gas exchange occurs across the surface so the area needs to be large.

Large surface area

Moist surface

Gas exchange takes place more readily across a moist cell membrane that across a dry one.

The alveoli have very thin walls

Thin walls offer least resistance to diffusion.

There is a very rich blood supply

Warm blooded organisms have high rates of carbon dioxide production and oxygen demand and therefore much blood must pass each second.

Tidal flow

Ribs — form a flexible cage for some of the muscles of ventilation to attach to; provide good protection against bruising for heart, kidneys and lungs

External and internal intercostals — external intercostal muscles lower the rib cage when they contract i.e. decrease its volume

internal intercostals raise the rib cage (increase its volume)

Diaphragm and its muscles — can flatten to increase lung volume, separates two body compartments

Abdominal muscles — raise the diaphragm into a dome so reducing lung volume (the intestines transfer the push from the flattened abdominal muscles to the diaphragm)

Intercostals are the part we eat when we have spare ribs

Two diagrams showing ribs, spine diaphragm , lungs and trachea

breathing in
the ribs lifted upwards and outwards
diaphragm flattened

breathing out
the ribs lowered downwards and inwards
diaphragm pushed upwards by the abdominal muscles

We can use either the rib muscles, or diaphragm and abdominal muscles or use both. We use both systems when deep breathing is needed.

Air in — lung volume increases

therefore the distance between gas particles increases

because the particles are travelling at around 400 meters per second all of this happens very quickly

gas particles that happen to be heading towards the lungs travel further before a collision (on average)

there is therefore a general movement of gas particles inwards

try to avoid vague answers like 'the muscles contract and so the gas is squeezed out'. At the level of the gas particles it is a matter of how far a particle moves before a collision. Gas particles are definitely not being squeezed from behind! They also do not **'want'** to go anywhere!

Tidal air flows in and out of the lungs

A graph showing the volumes of air breathed in and out by an adult human

lung volume (dm³)

6.0
3.4
3.0
1.5

normal relaxed breathing at rest

deepest breath in and then out that we can manage

we need to fall under a large roller to get this last bit of air out !

time

Changes in the composition of the air as humans breathe

Gas	Percentage composition of gas in:		
	air breathed in	air breathed out	alveolar air
Oxygen	20.93	16.89	14.50
Nitrogen	79.04	79.61	79.95
Carbon dioxide	0.03	3.50	5.55

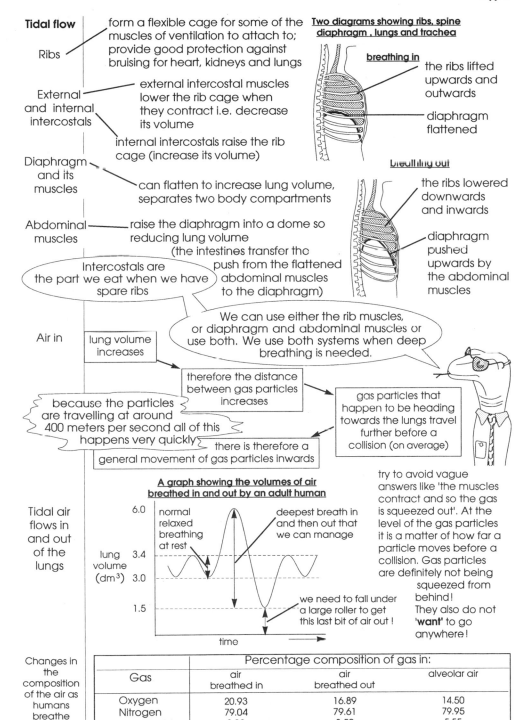

Humans as organisms | respiration

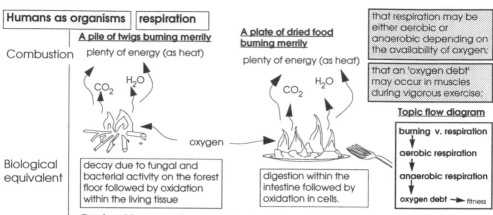

	A pile of twigs burning merrily	A plate of dried food burning merrily	that respiration may be either aerobic or anaerobic depending on the availability of oxygen;
Combustion	plenty of energy (as heat) CO₂ H₂O oxygen	plenty of energy (as heat) CO₂ H₂O	that an 'oxygen debt' may occur in muscles during vigorous exercise;

Topic flow diagram

burning v. respiration
↓
aerobic respiration
↓
anaerobic respiration
↓
oxygen debt → fitness

Biological equivalent

decay due to fungal and bacterial activity on the forest floor followed by oxidation within the living tissue

digestion within the intestine followed by oxidation in cells.

Dry food burns well outside the body, transferring the energy in the substances to heat very rapidly. Much too rapidly, in fact, to be of use for living tissue.
In living tissue of plants & animals, enzymes are used to allow a gradual transfer of energy from the food substances to ATP (**ATP** is widely used as an energy transfer molecule for nerve conduction, muscle action, active transport of substances across membranes etc.).

Word equations for respiration

Aerobic Carbohydrate + Oxygen ⟶ Carbon dioxide + Water (energy)

Anaerobic
Carbohydrate ⟶ Ethanol + Carbon dioxide (this happens in plants) (energy)

or Carbohydrate ⟶ Lactic acid (this happens in animal tissue) (energy)

A comparison of the energy released by our three main food types

Polymer	Atoms present in the molecule	Building Blocks	Energy released on burning
Carbohydrates	C, H, O	Simple sugars	17 kJ. per g.
Fats	C, H, & a little O	Fatty acids & glycerol	39 kJ. per g.
Proteins	C, H, N, O, & a little S	Amino acids	17 kJ. per g.

'oxygen debt'

A hardworking muscle (or tree root cells in water-logged soil) may be using oxygen faster than it can be supplied. All is not lost however as muscles can transfer energy without oxygen for a while. The problem is that lactic acid will build up in the animals tissue lowering the pH and this will cause damage.
Oxygen is needed to remove the lactic acid which is why we continue to pant for quite a while after exercise (our tissues are using a lot of the extra oxygen to remove the lactic acid). It is called oxygen debt because the tissues that have been working very hard are 'owed' oxygen.

'oxygen debt' and getting fit

Lower levels of oxygen stimulate the formation of new capillaries. Once these have formed, the blood supply will be better and so the muscle is able to work harder i.e. it is fitter!
Unfit people build up a large oxygen debt during exercise and will need to keep panting for quite a while after they stop working. Their hearts will carry on beating rapidly as well.
We can use the time taken for our heart rate to return to normal after exercise as a measure of fitness. Your heart will be back to your norma rate in two minutes provided that you are very fit. (see also the top of page 15)

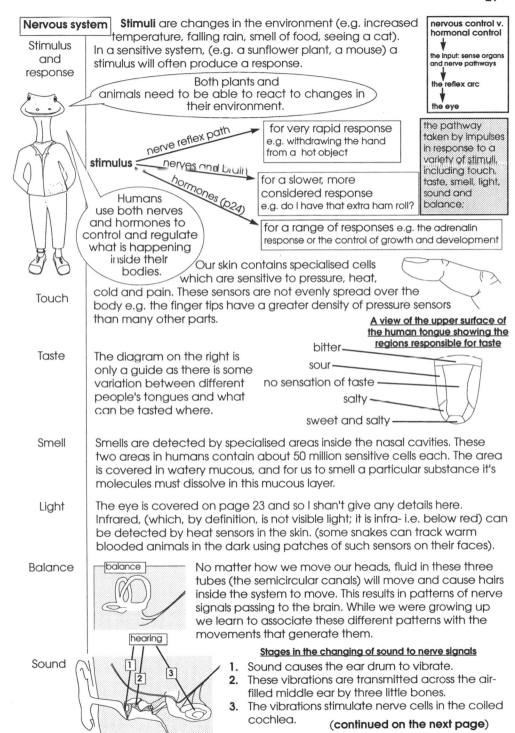

Nervous system | **Stimuli** are changes in the environment (e.g. increased temperature, falling rain, smell of food, seeing a cat). In a sensitive system, (e.g. a sunflower plant, a mouse) a stimulus will often produce a response.

nervous control v. hormonal control

↓

the input: sense organs and nerve pathways

↓

the reflex arc

↓

the eye

Stimulus and response

Both plants and animals need to be able to react to changes in their environment.

stimulus —

nerve reflex path → for very rapid response e.g. withdrawing the hand from a hot object

nerves and brain → for a slower, more considered response e.g. do I have that extra ham roll?

hormones (p24) → for a range of responses e.g. the adrenalin response or the control of growth and development

the pathway taken by impulses in response to a variety of stimuli, including touch, taste, smell, light, sound and balance;

Humans use both nerves and hormones to control and regulate what is happening inside their bodies.

Touch Our skin contains specialised cells which are sensitive to pressure, heat, cold and pain. These sensors are not evenly spread over the body e.g. the finger tips have a greater density of pressure sensors than many other parts.

Taste The diagram on the right is only a guide as there is some variation between different people's tongues and what can be tasted where.

A view of the upper surface of the human tongue showing the regions responsible for taste

bitter
sour
no sensation of taste
salty
sweet and salty

Smell Smells are detected by specialised areas inside the nasal cavities. These two areas in humans contain about 50 million sensitive cells each. The area is covered in watery mucous, and for us to smell a particular substance it's molecules must dissolve in this mucous layer.

Light The eye is covered on page 23 and so I shan't give any details here. Infrared, (which, by definition, is not visible light; it is infra- i.e. below red) can be detected by heat sensors in the skin. (some snakes can track warm blooded animals in the dark using patches of such sensors on their faces).

Balance balance

No matter how we move our heads, fluid in these three tubes (the semicircular canals) will move and cause hairs inside the system to move. This results in patterns of nerve signals passing to the brain. While we were growing up we learn to associate these different patterns with the movements that generate them.

hearing

Stages in the changing of sound to nerve signals

Sound

1. Sound causes the ear drum to vibrate.
2. These vibrations are transmitted across the air-filled middle ear by three little bones.
3. The vibrations stimulate nerve cells in the coiled cochlea.

(continued on the next page)

Humans as organisms | **nervous system**

Loudness and pitch

Hi Mum!

This organ (i.e. the ear) is able to respond to sound in the range 20 Hz. to 20,000 Hz. i.e. it can hear very low and very high notes, but it gets less sensitive with age and it can be damaged by regular loud noise (loud personal stereos etc.). Ears work because they can use mechanical vibrations to make signals pass along nerves to the brain. Pitch is distinguished because high notes stimulate nerve endings at the base of the cochlea (the part nearest the round and oval windows), whereas low notes are sensed by parts of the cochlea furthest from the oval window.

Loud sounds cause many signals per second to pass to the brain

Sound as vibrating air → Causes ear drum to vibrate → Causes ear bones to vibrate → Causes ear fluid to vibrate → nerve signals pass to the brain for analysis

A diagram of the human brain showing the parts that are visible from the left hand side

this region is involved in the conscious control of muscle activity (i.e. voluntary motor)

The brain

foot
leg
head and eye
arm
hand
skin
speech and co-ordination
tongue
hearing
word understanding
vision

signals that arrive in this region make us aware of sensations

the cerebellum It keeps a running record of how contracted each muscle is and the state of every joint. Before signals are sent out to the muscles they first pass through here for checking. There is no sense in asking a muscle to contract if it is already contracted!

the medulla oblongata This region of the brain controls vital functions like breathing and heart rate and blood pressure. Serious damage to it results in death

A diagram of a sensory neurone (with insulating cells around the dendrite)

A sensory neurone and a motor neurone

signal direction

A diagram of a motor neurone (with insulating cells around the axon)

signal direction

The reflex arc

A firm, but not fierce blow here

how the reflex arc, which involves a nerve impulse carried via neurones and across synapses, makes possible rapid responses to a stimulus;

spinal cord

nerve

Testing reflexes

When the tendon is struck (a gentle but firm blow), the muscle is stretched. Signals then pass from the stretch receptors on the muscle, along the sensory neurone, to the spine. Inside the spine the signal is split. One set of impulses pass across a short neurone and back to the muscle along a motor neurone whereupon the muscle contracts. The split signal passes up to the brain, making the person aware of what has happened. Our bodies use this sort of reflex to keep adjusting our position as we sit, stand or move. The blink reflex serves a protective function making us blink when any object approaches the eye.

(not to scale)

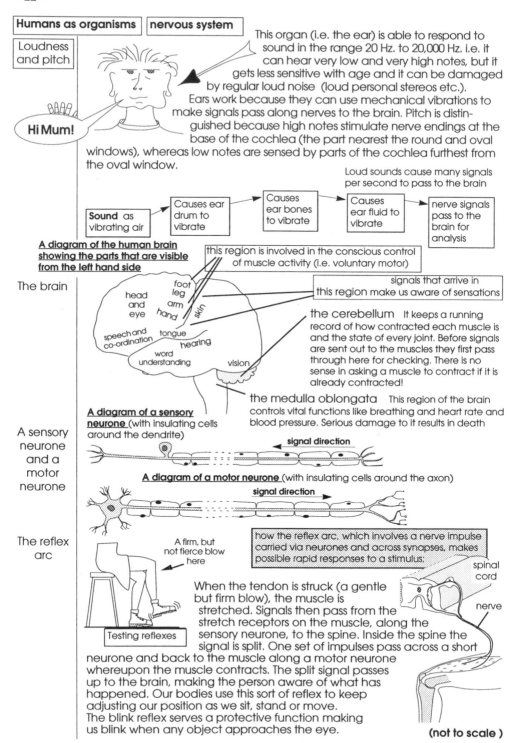

The eye

A diagram showing a horizontal slice though the human eye.

ciliary muscle

iris

lens

aqueous humour

cornea —
most of the bending of light takes place here. The lens just does the fine tuning of focus

This is important

blind spot

optic nerve

fovea centralis

retina

vitreous humour

The nerve and blood supply do not cover this region as happens elsewhere. Light passes directly to the light sensitive cells without having to pass through other tissue first.

sclera   A tough coat covering the eye.

Focussing the light

The rays of light coming from the image are bent by the cornea, then focussed by the lens (muscles can change the power of the lens), so that a sharp, upside-down image appears on the retina (which is inverted by the brain). Light sensitive cells (rods and cones) send nerve signals to the brain.

Detecting the light

Each retina is made up of about 70 million light sensitive cells.
Cones, are sensitive to different colours, and occur mainly at the back of the retina, directly in line with the lens.
Rods are very sensitive to light of any colour. Our eyes use rods for seeing in poor light.

Controlling the amount of light reaching the retina

The eye can see in starlight but also in bright sunlight. The variation in intensity of the light is huge! The rods and cones must be protected from very bright light and our eyes protect them by adjusting the size of the pupil. In very bright light the pupil is tiny and the iris is very obvious. Muscles in the iris adjust pupil size. As the iris is filled with pigment it can block out the surplus light. (This pigment gives our eyes their characteristic colour).

Long and short sight

Long sight

The cornea is not strongly curved or the eyeball is too short and so light from nearby objects is focussed behind the retina

We correct long sight by using convex lenses in front of the eyes

Short sight

The cornea is too strongly curved or the eyeball is too long and so light from distant objects is bent too sharply and is focussed in front of the retina

We correct short sight by using concave lenses in front of the eyes

Humans as organisms | hormones

Hormones

Hormones are chemical messengers, e.g. a substance produced in the brain of mammals, is carried by the blood to all parts of the body but produces its effect in the kidney where it reduces the flow of urine (antidiuretic hormone).

Flow chart

Hormones in humans (some of them anyway) → insulin, sex hormones, adrenaline

Medical uses for hormones

Fertility hormones

1. Hormones are synthesised in cells and released into the blood.
2. Carried by the blood, they reach most parts of the body but they produce their effect only on certain organs (the target organs).
3. A feedback mechanism makes sure that they stop being made once they have produced the required effect.
4. Hormones are constantly being removed from the body (many are degraded in the liver) for otherwise their concentration in the body would continue to increase.
5. Hormones produce their effects in anything from a few seconds, to months or years.

When reading about insulin keep referring back to the five points listed here.

Insulin

The pancreas (shown on the diagram on page 4 and again on page 13) has two main functions.
1. It produces enzymes and sodium hydrogen carbonate which are released into the small intestine during digestion. These are released down a duct.
2. Certain cells in the pancreas produce insulin which is released into the surrounding blood vessels.
3. This insulin is released when the levels of glucose in the blood are higher than normal.
4. The insulin has two effects: **a.** It causes the liver cells to store glucose as glycogen (an insoluble polyglucose).
   b. It allows glucose to pass into muscle and fat cells.
5. Both these effects will cause the glucose levels in the blood to fall and so insulin will stop being produced. (normal blood glucose levels: 0.95g dm^{-3})

The sex hormones

| Oestrogen & progesterone (produced in the ovaries) | Hormones that are important in the reproductive cycle of mammals. They can stimulate the development of breasts and other changes typical at puberty. |

| Testosterone (produced in the testes) | A group of male sex hormones. They cause the effects seen at puberty: increased deposition of muscle, development of genitals, growth of body hair and more. |

Adrenaline (the effects of releasing adrenaline into the blood)

Dilation of pupils	Allows more light to enter the eyes
Causes the hair to stand on end	
Relaxes the bronchioles	Increases the rate of gas exchange
Inhibits digestion and peristalsis	
Prevents bladder contraction	
Increases the rate and amplitude of the heartbeat	Improves the supply of blood to muscles so the blood pressure rises
Causes constriction of most blood vessels	
Stimulates the conversion of liver glycogen to glucose	So that there is a ready supply of glucose for muscle activity
Decreases sensory threshold	So the animal is more sensitive to pain
Increases mental awareness	

Medical uses

> If the hormones intended for treatment have been extracted from human tissue, they must be very carefully checked for hepatitis or HIV virus.

> Looking back to the bottom of the last page it is worth noting that adrenaline, on its own, will not produce any sensible activity. For this we need the nervous system to act.

Dwarfism	Hormones can be used to promote growth in very short people (treated while they are still young).
Diabetes	Insulin can be used to treat diabetes; people with this condition have little ability to regulate the levels of glucose in their blood stream.

some medical uses of hormones, including the control and promotion of fertility and the treatment of diabetes;

1. People who first suffered from diabetes when they were young will probably need to have twice daily injections of insulin. (they can't take insulin by mouth as it would be digested). The insulin needs to be carefully administered, an overdose will cause glucose to disappear from the blood and their nervous systems will suffer very quickly from a shortage of energy (an insulin-induced coma).

2. People who became diabetic later in life (late onset diabetes) often do not need insulin. They are able to control the condition by making changes to their diet.

Fertility

Some women are unable to fall pregnant because, though their ovaries contain viable eggs, these are not released. The maturation and release of such eggs can be encouraged by administering hormones normally secreted by the brain tissue.

Changes in the blood levels of oestrogen and progesterone

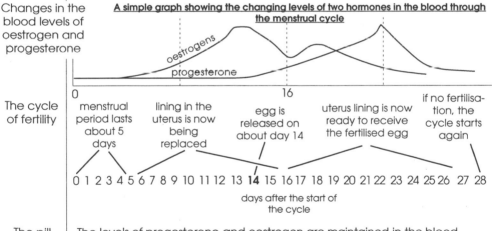

A simple graph showing the changing levels of two hormones in the blood through the menstrual cycle

oestrogens

progesterone

0   16

The cycle of fertility

menstrual period lasts about 5 days

lining in the uterus is now being replaced

egg is released on about day 14

uterus lining is now ready to receive the fertilised egg

if no fertilisation, the cycle starts again

0 1 2 3 4 5 6 7 8 9 10 11 12 13 **14** 15 16 17 18 19 20 21 22 23 24 25 26 27 28

days after the start of the cycle

The pill

The levels of progesterone and oestrogen are maintained in the blood during pregnancy, and these levels prevent the release of any more eggs by controlling the release of hormones from the brain.

No eggs . . . no unwanted fertilisation

By raising the levels of these hormones in the blood (i.e. by taking the pill) the release of eggs can be prevented. The pill is the most effective way of controlling fertility but it offers no protection against sexually transmitted diseases. (In theory not engaging in sex should be the most effective form of birth control, but in humans love making has a very important role in strengthening the bond between the partners).

Control	The speed of steam engines, the temperature of reactor cores, the water level in lavatory cisterns, population size, body temperature, and blood sugar levels are usually controlled within certain narrow limits (i.e. kept nearly constant).
Negative feedback.	Negative feed–back is used to control the size of any fluctuations (e.g. insulin is released from the pancreas when blood glucose levels rise, the insulin causes the levels to fall and so further release of insulin is halted).

Flow chart

Positive feedbacks can quickly result in disasters (e.g. The chip pan boils over, the fat catches fire and heats the pan further so more boils over adding to the flames and so on . . .)

Homeostasis i.e. feedback controls

↓

Specific examples CO_2, urea and bile

↓

Kidney function → dialysis

↓

temperature control

The three elastic bands (in the diagram) provide a stabilising **negative feedback**. The more the shape topples, the more the band is stretched and so the more the shape is pulled back into position.

A diagram to show how negative feedback can maintain the position of a cone

Unstable shape is being kept in equilibrium by negative feedback from the elastic bands

Homeostasis	This term is used for the control of the internal environment of organisms (plants, animals, fungi, bacteria etc) by means of negative feedback mechanisms (e.g. controlling body temperature, urea levels in the blood, blood pressure, carbon dioxide levels in the tissues).
The need for control	We are what we are because negative feedbacks keep our internal environment different from that outside ourselves.

If you doubt the need for control, take ten deep breaths quite quickly and see how strange you feel.

1. Breathing in and out deeply, removes lots of CO_2 from the blood.
2. Losing CO_2 means that the blood pH will rise.
3. Your brain works best only at certain pH levels and so you feel odd.

Until you breathed deeply your breathing rate was correct for the amount of CO_2 being produced in your tissues. Had you begun to exercise the rate would have increased automatically. These controls are going on constantly in our bodies, usually without our being aware of them.

	Factor	'Forces' for change	Stabilising 'forces'
Some important factors that need to be regulated in our bodies	CO_2 levels	Levels are affected by the rate at which CO_2 is produced in the tissues due to respiration.	Controlled by adjusting the rate at which we breath.
	Water content	Increased by drinking and eating, decreased by sweating, losing water when we breath out and losing water in the urine and faeces.	Adjusted by altering the concentration of the urine produced. We produce a very concentrated urine when short of water. We can also drink more or less fluid.
	The correct ions and in the right places	Taken in with the food and drink and lost mainly in sweat and urine, they also leak across cell membranes tending to make concentration equal inside and out.	The kidneys control the concentrations of different ions in the blood. Cell membranes are always busy keeping potassium ions inside cells and sodium ions outside them.

continued on page 27

continued from p 26

More important factors that need to be regulated in our bodies (the list contains more than you really need to know but even more examples could have been included)

Factor	'Forces' for change	Stabilising 'forces'
Body temperature	Increased by the rate at which tissue (mainly muscles and liver) are working, and decreased by heat loss from the body from the skin and by breathing out.	The blood supply to the skin can be changed so that it radiates more or less heat. We can also change our metabolic rate and begin shivering or sweating.
Hormone levels	Hormones are produced and released as needed. Their concentration will tend to rise.	They are broken down in the liver and then excreted.
Blood pressure	Increasing heart rate and constricting the diameter of small blood vessels will raise blood pressure and vica versa. Very low blood pressure means that pressure filtration stops in the kidneys and in the capillaries all over the body. It also means that the brain will run short of nutrients making the person feel faint.	

The origin and elimination of

carbon dioxide

urea

bile

all cells of the body produce carbon dioxide (CO_2) when the digested food molecules are further transformed.

how waste products of body functions are removed by the lungs and kidneys;

the CO_2 is a waste product and is excreted from the lungs

liver cells produce urea steadily as result of dealing with the building blocks of proteins (amino acids)

the urea is then carried to all parts of the body by the blood

the kidneys excrete most of the urea

liver cells also break down red blood cells and turn part of the haemoglobin into an excretory product (bile pigments)

bile is excreted from the liver

vein

20 to 30g. of urea are excreted from the kidneys each day

how the kidneys regulate the water content of the body;

The kidney at work

Excretion in the kidneys has two phases:
1. Force out water and small molecules in the glomeruli. Keep larger molecules (proteins etc) in the blood.
2. Reabsorb the small molecules that are important to the body e.g. amino acids and glucose, further down the tubule.

artery

A diagram showing activity in a kidney tubule

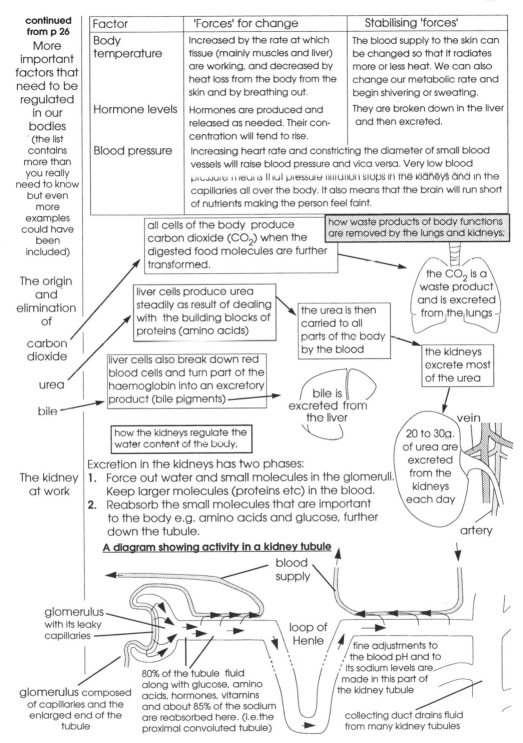

blood supply

glomerulus with its leaky capillaries

loop of Henle

fine adjustments to the blood pH and to its sodium levels are made in this part of the kidney tubule

glomerulus composed of capillaries and the enlarged end of the tubule

80% of the tubule fluid along with glucose, amino acids, hormones, vitamins and about 85% of the sodium are reabsorbed here. (i.e.the proximal convoluted tubule)

collecting duct drains fluid from many kidney tubules

Humans as organisms | **homeostasis**

Renal dialysis

People whose kidneys have failed, have to rely on a machine (a dialysis machine) to remove surplus water and unwanted molecules (e.g. urea, degraded hormones, excess sodium) from their blood.

The machine passes the blood through tubes made of selectively permeable membrane, keeping it warm at the same time, and allows the small molecules to diffuse out of the blood.

Renal dialysis v. kidney transplant

Whenever possible, doctors will try to replace damaged kidneys, as this frees the patients from dependence on a machine for their survival and also because, when it works, a kidney graft operation costs less than the cost of keeping a person on dialysis, even just for a year.

When explaining the role of the kidney try hard not to use vague terms like 'purify the blood' when really you mean 'remove unwanted substances'.

A diagram of a small part of the selectively permeable membrane used in a dialysis machine.

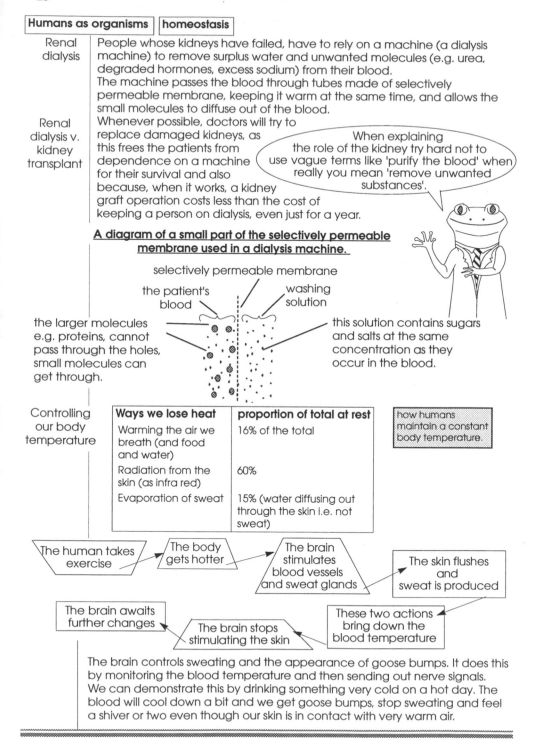

selectively permeable membrane

the patient's blood

washing solution

the larger molecules e.g. proteins, cannot pass through the holes, small molecules can get through.

this solution contains sugars and salts at the same concentration as they occur in the blood.

Controlling our body temperature

Ways we lose heat	proportion of total at rest
Warming the air we breath (and food and water)	16% of the total
Radiation from the skin (as infra red)	60%
Evaporation of sweat	15% (water diffusing out through the skin i.e. not sweat)

how humans maintain a constant body temperature.

The human takes exercise → The body gets hotter → The brain stimulates blood vessels and sweat glands → The skin flushes and sweat is produced

The brain awaits further changes ← The brain stops stimulating the skin ← These two actions bring down the blood temperature

The brain controls sweating and the appearance of goose bumps. It does this by monitoring the blood temperature and then sending out nerve signals. We can demonstrate this by drinking something very cold on a hot day. The blood will cool down a bit and we get goose bumps, stop sweating and feel a shiver or two even though our skin is in contact with very warm air.

health

Infections and protection

Protecting ourselves from infection
↓
Abusing our bodies

KS3 2r that bacteria and viruses can affect health,

the defence mechanisms of the body, including the role of the skin, blood and mucous membranes of the respiratory tract;

We live in a hostile world and need to have barriers that exclude organisms that might invade our bodies.

- dry layer of skin (on the outside)
- bacteria are trapped in layers of mucous lining the respiratory tract
- mobile cells that can engulf bacteria (i.e. macrophages) (in the lungs)

We also need mechanisms for dealing with those that manage to get past the first defences.

- a system of substances that kill invading agents e.g. bacteria and viruses (i.e. antibodies in the blood)
- another set of substances that neutralise toxins released by the invading organisms
- cells that can engulf the invading agents (e.g. the marcrophages found in our livers that engulf such organisms as they flow past, carried by the blood).

A diagram showing a vertical slice through the skin

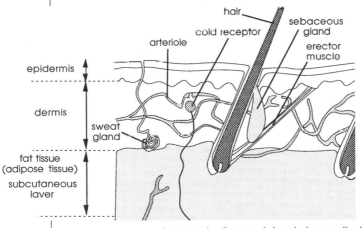

hair
sebaceous gland
cold receptor
arteriole
erector muscle
epidermis
dermis
sweat gland
fat tissue (adipose tissue)
subcutaneous laver

Our skin carries its own population of bacteria, and these may be releasing substances that prevent the growth of other micro-organsims.
Skin which remains damp for any time easily becomes infected
e.g. athletes foot occurs between the toes.

Openings

Eyes and mouth — tears and saliva contain substances that have anti-microbial properties.

Respiratory tract
1. Mucous being moved outwards all the time by beating cilia. Dust and bacteria are moved along at about 0.4mm a second. About 100 cm^3 of mucous is produced each day (most of this is swallowed).
2. Phagocytes engulf any small particles that reach the lungs.

Digestive tract — Acid in the stomach kills most of the infectious agents that are taken in with the food.

vagina — certain bacteria live naturally here and make the conditions slightly acid (pH 4), thus preventing the growth of other agents.

Any opening in the body provides a route for infections.

| Humans as organisms | health |

the effects of solvents, alcohol, tobacco and other drugs on body functions.

Solvent abuse

People have found that it is possible to get a weird feeling by breathing in the fumes given off from certain glues. These fumes contain the solvent for the glue. They dissolve in fats and may be carried by the blood from lungs to nervous system where they affect the membranes of neurones and so produce their harmful effect.

Alcohol

It is illegal in the U.K. to sell alcoholic drinks (wine, beer, spirits etc) to anyone who is under 18.

It is also illegal for people to drink alcoholic drinks at the place of sale unless it has a licence which allows this.

There are some good reasons for all of these restrictions. **Most of us will, at some stage in our lives, have an uneasy relationship with alcohol.** 'Most of us' means you and me. It seems that the hardest thing for people to admit to, is that they have a problem at all. Alcohol depresses the activity in the nervous system and therefore makes us feel less inhibited. If that is all that it did, there would be no problem, but alcohol is poisonous. Regular doses over many years bring about changes in the brain and liver cells so that many of these cells die, causing loss of memory and intellectual ability and loss of liver function.

If a heavy drinker stops taking alcohol, the nervous system reacts by becoming very active. The patient begins trembling within 12 hours and then there can be severe restlessness, anxiety, fierce hallucinations, disorientation and confusion.

(**Present estimates for the U.K. population are that about 1 in 500 adults are chronic alcoholics**). Remember that most alcoholics carry on with their jobs and get quite skilled at hiding the signs of their problems from the rest of us.

The cost to industry and families can be very high due to absence from work, reduced ability to work due to hangovers and violence in the home, having to clean carpets and mattresses because the alcoholic has poor bladder control as well as all the financial problems that heavy drinking bring in its wake.

Meths.

Methanol (or alcohol to which methanol has been added e.g industrial spirit) should never be used as a drink. The body reacts to methanol by changing it to formic acid or formaldehyde. Both of these are toxic, 15 cm^3 is enough to cause serious poisoning.

Smoking

bronchitis (growth of bacteria in damaged lining of the bronchus and bronchioles).

cancers mainly of the lungs and oesophagus (in 1776, the London surgeon, Pott, showed that something in soot caused cancer in chimney sweeps so the link between substances in smoke and cancer has been known for a long time).

arterial disease

having generally reduced efficiency
1. Substances in the smoke damage the lungs so that gas exchange is less rapid.
2. Carbon monoxide (in ciggy smoke) combines permanently with haemoglobin so that there is less haemoglobin to carry oxygen.

Effects of smoking

being the big turnoff to about half the population by smelling like yesterday's ashtray

Addiction, dependence, Heroin, Morphine, Speed, etc.

For many thousands of years, people have been using alcohol and marihuana (hash) to change their mood . They have also been having trouble with alcohol abuse for many thousands of years. Purified opium (heroin and morphine), L.S.D., amphetamines and barbiturates have been a cause of problems mainly within this century.

We can define **addiction** as the stage reached by a person when their need for regular doses of their particular drug (alcohol, cocaine etc.) begins to interfere with their physical well-being or with their job. Their relationships with people who are close to them are also affected.

Before we begin this section, we must explain the difference between a **chemical** and a **psychological** dependence on a drug (often drugs produce both sorts of dependence).

In **chemical** dependence, the person's body has made adjustments to its chemistry so that the drug has become essential. Breaking the habit can be very unpleasant, with fevers, nasty hallucinations, shakes and nausea. A person with a **psychological** dependence on a drug _feels_ that the drug is essential to help them get through each day.

Heroin and **Morphine** are derived from opium poppy sap.They are both savage drugs. Heroin causes severe deterioration in personality and behaviour. The person's need to get regular amounts of their drug can become so pressing that they will steal or prostitute themselves to get the necessary money.

A real danger with street drugs is that we don't know what else is in them.

Amphetamine ('Speed') and **Methedrine** are stimulants that induce feelings of well being with a sense of abundant physical energy. True chemical dependence does not occur, but people can suffer from severe depression when they stop taking the drug. Steady heavy use can produce symptoms like a persecution complex with hallucinations.

Ecstacy The effects of this are similar to LSD. It is hallucinogenic in large amounts, but low quantities give the feeling of having lots of energy (with bouts of depression over the next few days). At higher doses it mimics amphetamines. Ecstacy is not physically addictive but there is a danger of overheating and sudden collapse due to dehydration.

Health (the final bit) Bacteria and viruses

Make a real effort to learn the difference between bacteria, shown on the right, and viruses, which are much simpler, often being only a bit of DNA or RNA wrapped in protein. Notice the difference is size.

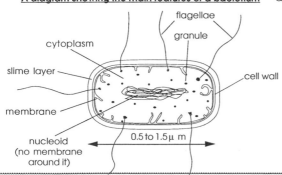

A diagram showing the main features of a bacterium

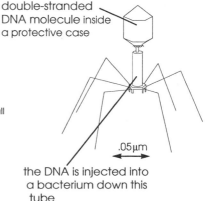

A diagram showing the structure of one type of virus (this one infects bacteria)

| Green plants as organisms | nutrition |

Photosynthesis

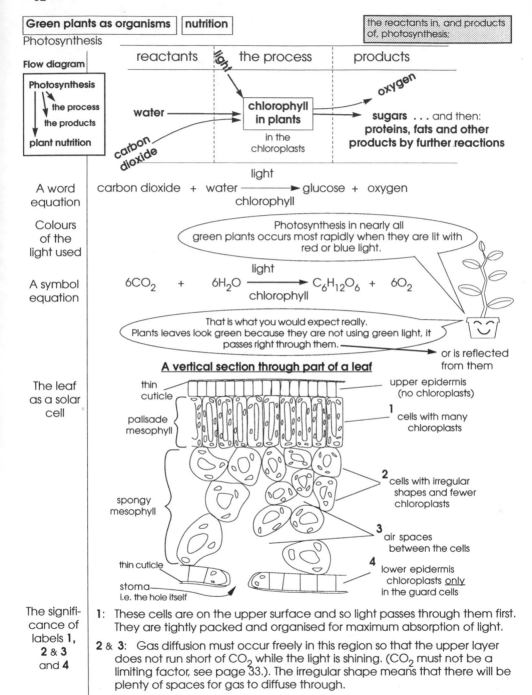

Flow diagram

Photosynthesis
→ the process
→ the products
plant nutrition

reactants   light   **the process**   **products**

water — → **chlorophyll in plants** in the chloroplasts → oxygen

carbon dioxide →

→ **sugars** ... and then: **proteins, fats and other products by further reactions**

A word equation

$$\text{carbon dioxide} + \text{water} \xrightarrow[\text{chlorophyll}]{\text{light}} \text{glucose} + \text{oxygen}$$

Colours of the light used

Photosynthesis in nearly all green plants occurs most rapidly when they are lit with red or blue light.

A symbol equation

$$6CO_2 + 6H_2O \xrightarrow[\text{chlorophyll}]{\text{light}} C_6H_{12}O_6 + 6O_2$$

That is what you would expect really. Plants leaves look green because they are not using green light, it passes right through them.

or is reflected from them

A vertical section through part of a leaf

The leaf as a solar cell

thin cuticle

palisade mesophyll

spongy mesophyll

thin cuticle

stoma
i.e. the hole itself

upper epidermis (no chloroplasts)

1 cells with many chloroplasts

2 cells with irregular shapes and fewer chloroplasts

3 air spaces between the cells

4 lower epidermis chloroplasts <u>only</u> in the guard cells

The significance of labels **1**, **2** & **3** and **4**

1: These cells are on the upper surface and so light passes through them first. They are tightly packed and organised for maximum absorption of light.

2 & 3: Gas diffusion must occur freely in this region so that the upper layer does not run short of CO_2 while the light is shining. (CO_2 must not be a limiting factor, see page 33.). The irregular shape means that there will be plenty of spaces for gas to diffuse through.

4: The guard cells use their chlorophyll as part of their opening and closing mechanism.

Optimising growth

Farmers try to organize things so that nothing is in short supply i.e. the plants are growing as fast as the available light allows.

We can use this idea to define the term **limiting factor** : A limiting factor is that which is holding back growth (or reaction speed, etc). In the case of a plant with yellowing leaves there may be plenty of light, space and water but there is too little nitrogen salts in the soil. These missing salts are the limiting factor.

Limiting factors

In the case of plants the limiting factor is whichever of these is in short supply.

- light
- carbon dioxide
- water
- minerals
- space to grow
- temperature

until a moment ago, water was the limiting factor here.

now water is plentiful and so growth rate has speeded up **until something else is in short supply**

how the products of photosynthesis are utilised by the plant

light
water
carbon dioxide

→ photo-synthesis → oxygen

→ **simple sugars e.g. glucose**

→ Joined together to make . . . → starch, cellulose, pectins, gums and resin.

→ chemically changed to form fatty acids → joined together to make . . . → fats and oils

→ joined with the nitrogen (from nitrogen compounds in the soil) to make . . . → amino acids → proteins

→ nucleic acids i.e. DNA or RNA

On this side there is nothing that could be called food ! Plants make food, they do not get food from the soil.

The role of minerals

A diagram showing the main minerals needed for healthy plant growth

Nitrogen in the form of **nitrates, nitrites or ammonium ions**.

Magnesium as **magnesium ions** .

Magnesium forms the central part of the chlorophyll molecule.

Nitrogen is an important part of the building blocks of :
1 proteins.
2 genetic chemicals e.g. DNA
3 chlorophyll

Phosphorus as **phosphate ions**.

Phosphate ions form part of DNA. They are a vital part of the ATP molecule.

Symptoms of a shortage: Stunted growth and yellowing of leaves

Potassium as **potassium ions**.

these are important for membrane function and during photosynthesis.

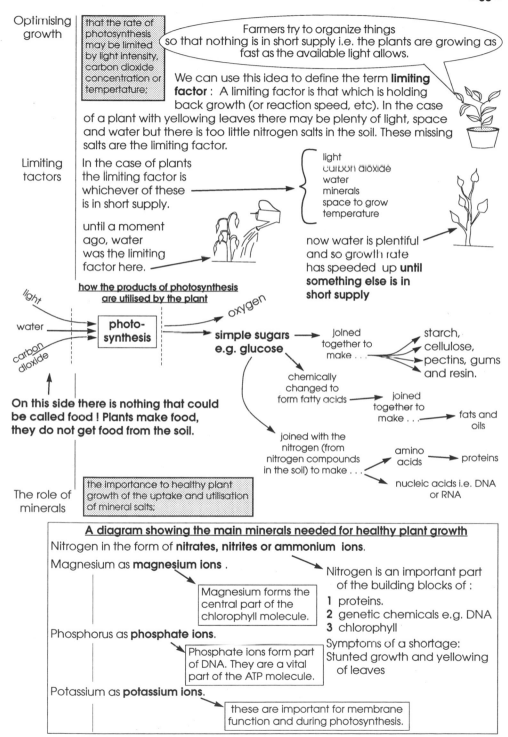

Green plants as organisms | nutrition

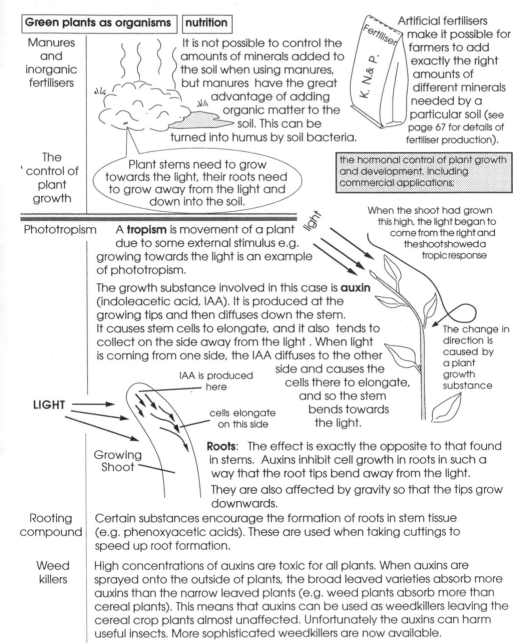

Manures and inorganic fertilisers

It is not possible to control the amounts of minerals added to the soil when using manures, but manures have the great advantage of adding organic matter to the soil. This can be turned into humus by soil bacteria.

Artificial fertilisers make it possible for farmers to add exactly the right amounts of different minerals needed by a particular soil (see page 67 for details of fertiliser production).

Fertiliser K, N & P.

The control of plant growth

Plant stems need to grow towards the light, their roots need to grow away from the light and down into the soil.

the hormonal control of plant growth and development, including commercial applications;

Phototropism

A **tropism** is movement of a plant due to some external stimulus e.g. growing towards the light is an example of phototropism.

The growth substance involved in this case is **auxin** (indoleacetic acid, IAA). It is produced at the growing tips and then diffuses down the stem. It causes stem cells to elongate, and it also tends to collect on the side away from the light. When light is coming from one side, the IAA diffuses to the other side and causes the cells there to elongate, and so the stem bends towards the light.

When the shoot had grown this high, the light began to come from the right and the shoot showed a tropic response

The change in direction is caused by a plant growth substance

IAA is produced here

LIGHT →

cells elongate on this side

Growing Shoot

Roots: The effect is exactly the opposite to that found in stems. Auxins inhibit cell growth in roots in such a way that the root tips bend away from the light.

They are also affected by gravity so that the tips grow downwards.

Rooting compound

Certain substances encourage the formation of roots in stem tissue (e.g. phenoxyacetic acids). These are used when taking cuttings to speed up root formation.

Weed killers

High concentrations of auxins are toxic for all plants. When auxins are sprayed onto the outside of plants, the broad leaved varieties absorb more than the narrow leaved plants (e.g. weed plants absorb more than cereal plants). This means that auxins can be used as weedkillers leaving the cereal crop plants almost unaffected. Unfortunately the auxins can harm useful insects. More sophisticated weedkillers are now available.

Contact and systemic weedkillers

A contact weedkiller kills those parts of the plant that are wet by the spray. A systemic weedkiller is absorbed into the tissues and spreads throughout the plant so that roots as well as leaves are killed.

Other uses

Auxins and other plant hormones are also used to prolong flowering, to prevent early fruit drop and to produce seedless grapes and seedless oranges.

| Green plants as organisms | transport and water relations |

Passage of water through a plant
(from soil to air)

(see page 3 for more detail on xylem and phloem)

Root hairs

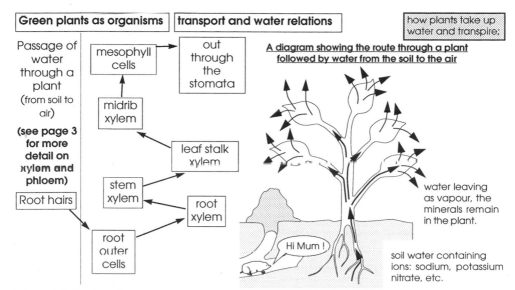

mesophyll cells → out through the stomata

midrib xylem

leaf stalk xylem

stem xylem ← root xylem

root outer cells

A diagram showing the route through a plant followed by water from the soil to the air

Hi Mum !

water leaving as vapour, the minerals remain in the plant.

soil water containing ions: sodium, potassium nitrate, etc.

More details of water movement

Root hairs and stomata

A diagram showing the main features of a root hair cell

root hair in <u>very</u> close contact with soil grains

soil particles (coated with water)

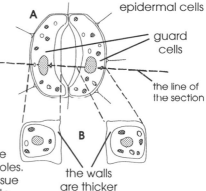

A diagram showing: a.) guard cells on the lower side of a leaf & b) in section

epidermal cells

A

guard cells

the line of the section

B

the walls are thicker here

Root hairs: Water passes in through the cell wall, the cytoplasm and the vacuoles. Further into the root there is a ring of tissue where the cell walls are impermeable to water (the Casparian strip) so that the cytoplasm can have some control over what elements are taken into the plant. (otherwise the plant would have to take up any elements in the soil, even poisonous ones)

Guard Cells: The cell wall structure is such that if the guard cells absorb water, they will bulge and open the stoma. They therefore bulge open when water is plentiful, close when the plant is short of water.

Factors that increase transpiration rate

1. Light.   The stomata open in the light and close in the dark. The brighter the light the more they are able to open (provided the plant is not short of water).
2. Increase in temperature.   Diffusion speeds up as the temperature rises.
3. Increase in air movement around the leaves.   This will have the effect of blowing away humid air from around the stomata.
4. Decrease in humidity.   The leaves will dry out faster when the air is dry.

Green plants as organisms | transport and water relations

Wilting

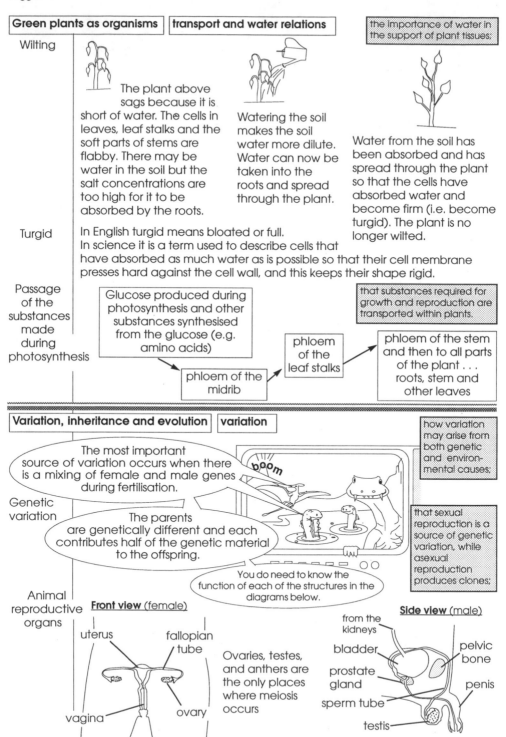

The plant above sags because it is short of water. The cells in leaves, leaf stalks and the soft parts of stems are flabby. There may be water in the soil but the salt concentrations are too high for it to be absorbed by the roots.

Watering the soil makes the soil water more dilute. Water can now be taken into the roots and spread through the plant.

Water from the soil has been absorbed and has spread through the plant so that the cells have absorbed water and become firm (i.e. become turgid). The plant is no longer wilted.

Turgid

In English turgid means bloated or full.
In science it is a term used to describe cells that have absorbed as much water as is possible so that their cell membrane presses hard against the cell wall, and this keeps their shape rigid.

Passage of the substances made during photosynthesis

that substances required for growth and reproduction are transported within plants.

Glucose produced during photosynthesis and other substances synthesised from the glucose (e.g. amino acids)

→ phloem of the midrib

→ phloem of the leaf stalks

→ phloem of the stem and then to all parts of the plant . . . roots, stem and other leaves

Variation, inheritance and evolution | variation

how variation may arise from both genetic and environmental causes;

The most important source of variation occurs when there is a mixing of female and male genes during fertilisation.

Genetic variation

The parents are genetically different and each contributes half of the genetic material to the offspring.

that sexual reproduction is a source of genetic variation, while asexual reproduction produces clones;

boom

You do need to know the function of each of the structures in the diagrams below.

Animal reproductive organs

Front view (female)

uterus

fallopian tube

vagina

ovary

Ovaries, testes, and anthers are the only places where meiosis occurs

Side view (male)

from the kidneys

bladder

prostate gland

sperm tube

pelvic bone

penis

testis

Plant reproductive organs

petal, stigma, anther, style, filament, sepal, carpel, receptacle, ovules

Pollen grains are not the plant's equivalent of sperm! The pollen grain germinates on the stigma, a pollen tube grows through the female tissue to the ovule. Fertilisation then takes place . . . a single nucleus from the pollen tube fuses with the nucleus of the ovule.

Nucleus

See pages 7 and 9 for quite a lot of detail. Best to read what is there before going on with fertilisation.

Sex cells

Sex cells (ova, male nuclei in pollen tubes, sperm) contain only one of each pair of chromosomes. A normal human ovum would have 23 chromosomes.

Fertilisation in humans (and other mammals)

Fertilisation itself occurs after a sperm meets the egg. This usually occurs in the fallopian tubes. The first viable sperm that contacts the outer surface of the egg causes a change in the outer surface, which prevent any more sperm from entering. Almost immediately after the sperm enters the egg, its chromosomes collect together with the egg chromosomes forming a nucleus. Development then begins.

Zygote

Zygote is the term used for a fertilised egg before it begins to divide to form the embryo. In most cases zygotes have both sets of chromosomes (e.g. human zygotes have 46 chromosomes).

Chromosomes, genes and protein synthesis.

Chromosomes, genes and protein synthesis are here together because they are so intimately linked. The genes are on the chromosomes and are responsible for protein synthesis.

Have a look at pages 7, 9 and 10 for some details.

The details that follow are really only needed by pupils aiming for the Higher Tier

DNA

Deoxyribonucleic acid (DNA) is the main substance of genetics and we need to have some idea of its structure.

the gene is a section of DNA

DNA is a long chain made by joining molecules. The sugar is deoxyribose, there is phosphate and then four similar molecules (bases) which form the information part of the genes.

sugar   phosphate   nitrogen-containing 'base'

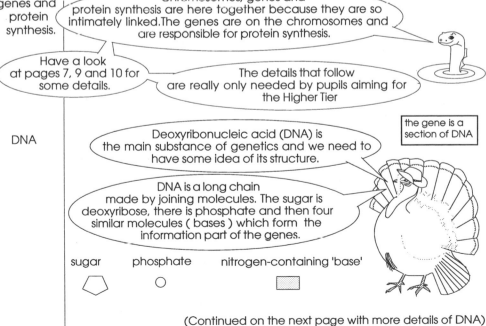

(Continued on the next page with more details of DNA)

Variation, inheritance and evolution | variation

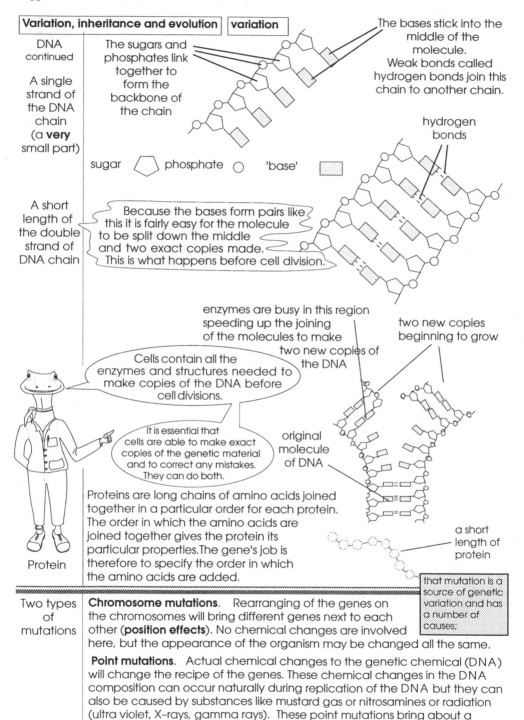

DNA continued

A single strand of the DNA chain (a very small part)

The sugars and phosphates link together to form the backbone of the chain

The bases stick into the middle of the molecule.
Weak bonds called hydrogen bonds join this chain to another chain.

hydrogen bonds

sugar ⬠ phosphate ◯ 'base' ▭

A short length of the double strand of DNA chain

Because the bases form pairs like this it is fairly easy for the molecule to be split down the middle and two exact copies made. This is what happens before cell division.

enzymes are busy in this region speeding up the joining of the molecules to make two new copies of the DNA

two new copies beginning to grow

Cells contain all the enzymes and structures needed to make copies of the DNA before cell divisions.

It is essential that cells are able to make exact copies of the genetic material and to correct any mistakes. They can do both.

original molecule of DNA

Protein

Proteins are long chains of amino acids joined together in a particular order for each protein. The order in which the amino acids are joined together gives the protein its particular properties. The gene's job is therefore to specify the order in which the amino acids are added.

a short length of protein

that mutation is a source of genetic variation and has a number of causes;

Two types of mutations

Chromosome mutations. Rearranging of the genes on the chromosomes will bring different genes next to each other (**position effects**). No chemical changes are involved here, but the appearance of the organism may be changed all the same.

Point mutations. Actual chemical changes to the genetic chemical (DNA) will change the recipe of the genes. These chemical changes in the DNA composition can occur naturally during replication of the DNA but they can also be caused by substances like mustard gas or nitrosamines or radiation (ultra violet, X-rays, gamma rays). These point mutations bring about a change in the proteins produced when genes are expressed.

inheritance x and y chromosomes	Humans have 23 pairs of chromosomes. Of these, 22 sets look as though they are part of a pair. That leaves two chromosomes, which are not similar. These determine sex and are called **x** and **y** chromosomes. The gametes contain either an **x** or a **y**. When gametes fuse at fertilisation the zygote must therefore be either **xx** or **xy**. Individuals with **xx** in all their cells are female. Individuals with **xy** in all their cells are male.

how gender is determined in humans;

Two definitions
dominant and recessive

Dominant As the name suggests, certain alleles are expressed even though they are present on only one of the pair of chromosomes. Such alleles (see below for a definition) are know as dominants.

the mechanism of monohybrid inheritance where there are dominant and recessive alleles;

Recessive Not all the genes/alleles are expressed. There are genes which do not show themselves unless they occur as a pair. Such genes are "recessive".

A genetic cross

The diagram below represents what happens to the genes when pure-breeding tall and dwarf pea plants are crossed. (The diagram ignores all the other genes in these two plants......the picture would become too complicated if we included them)

Let T stand for the "tall" gene and t stand for the "dwarf" gene:

Parents   TT   x   tt
Gametes   T   x   t
F_1 All the offspring are Tt   (they are all tall)

Next generation

Parents   Tt   x   Tt
Gametes   T   or   t   x   T   or   t

F_2 TT   Tt   Tt   tt

on average there are   3 tall   to every   1 short

More definitions

Homologous Having a structural similarity. It is not the same as identical.

Allele Simply stated, alleles are the different forms of a particular gene. Alleles occur at the same position on homologous chromosomes.

Gamete Another name for sex cells. (pollen grains, eggs, ova or sperm).

Genotype The genetic make-up of an organism. i.e. all the genes that an individual inherits.

Phenotype The appearance of an organism as well as its biochemical make-up.

Sex chromosome The 'pair' of chromosomes known as 'X' and 'Y'. These determine sex in many organisms. In humans, individuals with XX are female; if they have XY they are male.

Zygote When the egg and sperm fuse, a zygote has been formed which will then develop into a new organism.

Gene pool All the genes in a genetic population (a genetic population is a population in which it is theoretically possible for any individual to breed with any other). No one person will carry all the genes but they will all exist somewhere in the population.

| Variation, inheritance and evolution | inheritance |

Genetic diseases

Birth frequencies of some common conditions	
Condition	per 1000 live births
Huntington's Chorea (one form of madness)	0.8
Haemophilia	0.1
Non-specific severe mental retardation	0.5
Sickle cell anaemia (in Europe)	0.1

there are about 900 diseases known to be carried by dominant alleles with a total frequency of 7 per 1000 live births.

Clones

the basic principles of cloning, selective breeding and genetic engineering.

A clone is a copy of an organism that is genetically identical. It is now possible to make such clones. In theory, when we have bred the perfect dairy cow we can use genetic engineering and embryo manipulation techniques to produce herds of this cow.

In practice this is unlikely to happen on a large scale if only because humans are unlikely to agree as to what is 'the perfect dairy cow'. What is even less likely to happen is that humans will start producing large numbers of clones from the 'perfect human'; a creature who combines the features of Marie Curie, Einstein, Mozart, Miss World, the Chippendales and a whole lot of other remarkable people.

The plant kingdom provides us with many examples of clones. All plants made from cuttings are genetically identical and therefore are clones of the parent plant.

Genetic engineering

During genetic engineering, single genes or groups of genes are moved from one organism to another. The organisms do not have to be related. For example we can put human genes into bacteria so that the bacteria will produce large amounts of some useful substance e.g. insulin.

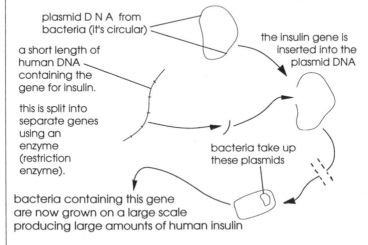

plasmid D N A from bacteria (it's circular)

a short length of human DNA containing the gene for insulin.

this is split into separate genes using an enzyme (restriction enzyme).

the insulin gene is inserted into the plasmid DNA

bacteria take up these plasmids

bacteria containing this gene are now grown on a large scale producing large amounts of human insulin

Some uses of genetic engineering

1. Production of **insulin** (the hormone needed by diabetics which until recently had to be extracted from animal pancreas obtained from the abattoir).

2. Production of the very powerful anti–viral and anti–cancer chemicals know as **lymphokines (e.g. interferon)**. These are normally produced by cells in our bodies but only in very small quantities.

Some more uses of genetic engineering	**3.** Production of large quantities of **enzymes** for use in industry e.g. the use of starch digesting enzymes to break down cheap starch from cereals (like maize or barley) into glucose syrup (try to find glucose syrup amongst the list of ingredients for sweet things to get some idea of how widespread it's use is). **4.** Inserting genes from different species which allow a crop plant to make it's own insecticide and therefore resist being eaten by insects. Many different plants produce insecticides. The trick is to get the insecticide produced by all tissues other than the ones we want e.g. the seeds in the case of beans or corn.
Selective breeding	Until genetic engineering became possible, we had to rely on breeding experiments to produce improved strains of plants or animals. For example we would keep choosing the best milk cows as breeding animals and so slowly improve the production of the dairy herd. Obviously, breeding experiments can only be done with organisms of the same species and it could take many years to produce the desired result. Producing a noticeably better herd of cows may take 30 years or so. In the case of plants this breeding program was greatly shortened when people discovered how to grow whole plants from just a few cells. This allowed people to grow many copies of the desired plant and so get large quantities of seed for the next generation. Because the tissue culture is carried out under ideal conditions the plants grow quickly enough for there to be several generations in each year. Genetic engineering has speeded up the process of improvement even more. We now move just the genes we want to move and can do it in a single generation but genetic engineering has raised many ethical problems.

---

evolution Some of the evidence for evolution	**1** Sedimentary rocks contain fossils (the durable remains, or casts of remains) of organisms that are no longer present on Earth. **2** Older sedimentary rocks contain fossils of a simpler nature. Rocks laid down 3000 million years ago contain evidence of the simplest forms of life (blue-green algae).

the fossil record as evidence for evolution.

Fossil record
↓
An outline of how evolution might work

Natural variations and evolution	**1.** There is always variation within a species (tall, short, fast, slow, fat, thin, able to withstand cold conditions better, more efficient user of food, etc).

how variation and selection may lead to evolution or to extinction.

	2. Because offspring so often resemble their parents, we know that these variations can be passed on.
Darwin / Wallace theory set out	**3.** There are always more offspring produced than can possibly survive so that, on average, it will be the 'best suited' who have the best chance of surviving (for every 2 blackbirds that survive to breed in your garden, about 10 will have died without breeding). **4.** This steady removal of organisms before they can breed (selection at work) will tend to stabilise the species keeping it suited to its environment. **5.** Provided the environment remains constant, there will be stability of species for long periods. However, if the environment changes (gets wetter, warmer, etc) then new models of existing organisms may appear and breed.

(continued on the next page)

Variation, inheritance and evolution | inheritance

People first thought that the changes from one species to another would be a gradual affair. This was a reasonable idea as such changes could be seen happening in agriculture (producing new varieties though not new species).

The current thinking is that, whilst species can evolve gradually into new forms, it is also just as possible for new species to appear quite suddenly due to reorganisation of the chromosomes rather than to gradual changes in the DNA.

Using adapt in discussions

Adapt as used in everyday English suggests the ability we all have to change our behaviour to suit new conditions.
When discussing evolution we say that a species can adapt to changes in the environment, but we don't mean that the members change their characteristics and so survive. What happens is that the unsuited members die, those that are genetically different enough to survive in the new conditions will do so and so the species adapts.

The selfish gene

If an organism does not breed, its own collection of genes are lost from the gene pool of its group. Genes which made their carriers indifferent to reproduction will therefore quickly be eliminated from a population. The converse is also true! Any genes which drive individuals to mate and so pass on their own genes will be very common.

The idea of the 'selfish gene' is that organisms are programmed to ensure that it is their genes which have the best chance of being passed on to the next generation. A lion, taking over a pride of lionesses will seek and kill all the cubs produced by the previous lion. This same behaviour is shown by Langur monkey males as well as by males of other species.

Until the idea of the selfish gene was suggested these last three examples of infanticide made very little sense.

(The idea of of a selfish gene may also help us to understand, but not to justify, the behaviour of some step parents who seem to treat their own children differently to the way that they treat their step children).

Genes and the environment (Nature and Nurture)

Organisms with identical genes can have very different appearances because of the effect of the environment. There are many examples of this but here are just two:
1. On rocks at the sea, the blue mussels that have managed to settle on a place below the mid-tide level grow much larger than those that have settled in the splash zone.
2. The weeds that manage to grow on a compacted path are much smaller than those of the same species growing on a recently cultivated soil, like a flower bed.

how variation may arise from both genetic and environmental causes;

| Living things in their environment | adaptation and competition |

Have another look at your Key Stage 3 notes on making keys for classifying groups of organisms.

Start this section by learning the definitions. We must always be able to define our terms.

Adaptation	Organisms only survive because they are perfectly adapted for all the conditions that occur in their environment. This means that most organisms are adapted for a particular habitat e.g. woodland, pond, river bed, grassland, rocky sea shore etc. Each of these habitats will have its own collection of organisms (see the top of p.42)
Biomass	The total quantity of matter in all the organisms (or in a particular species) that inhabit a region or trophic level.
Biosphere	The biosphere is that part of the atmosphere, earth and oceans where living organisms are found.
Carnivore	An animal that lives almost exclusively on the flesh of other animals.
Community	All the groups of organisms which occupy the same area, and which interact, make up a community. (Some species trap the energy in sunlight; others feed on them; and others are carnivorous). The pond community and woodland community provide good examples.
Competition	Any two species which eat the same food, or have similar lifestyles, and which occur in the same habitat, will be in competition for the things that they need. Competition is most fierce between members of the same species.
Habitat	A habitat is a well-defined locality where a set of organisms live. Moorland, for example, has heathers, grasses, sedges and a group of specific animals: grouse, certain insects, birds of prey, and so on.
Niche	A way of 'earning a living' within a community. No two species can occupy the same niche for any length of time for they are in direct competition and so sooner or later one species must dominate.
Predator	A predator captures and kills live animals for its food. In a typical food chain, the carnivores usually get larger as we move up the chain, e.g. fly → spider → shrew → owl
Parasite	A parasite lives on or within another creature and feeds on the creature, or on it's food (intestinal parasites). Only the parasite benefits from this relationship. It is a very specialised predator.
Saprophyte	Organisms which feed on dead or decaying organic matter are called saprophytes (mainly fungi and bacteria, i.e. decomposers).
Symbiosis	In this relationship, two organisms live very closely together, usually to the benefit of both, e.g. cellulose-digesting bacteria in the stomach of a cow.
Trophic level	Trophic levels are the steps through which energy is transferred as it moves through a food web. Each step, grazing, predation, parasitism, decomposition, provide us with a different trophic level.

Run for it Folks ! Owls mean trouble !

Living things in their environment | adaptation and competition

Adaptation

The graph on the right shows the sort of curve that would result if you made a random sample of 1000 starlings, weighed each one and then plotted frequency on the y axis and body weight on the x axis.

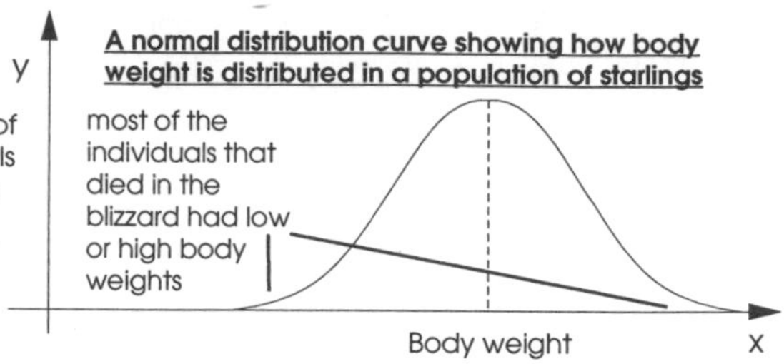

Number of individuals at each body weight

A normal distribution curve showing how body weight is distributed in a population of starlings

most of the individuals that died in the blizzard had low or high body weights

Body weight   x

People collected dead starlings after a blizzard, measured their body weight and compared these weights with the normal distribution. Most of dead starlings had body weights on the lower or higher edges of the distribution.

This same result has been found in other examples. When conditions are stressful, it is the average specimens that tend to survive best.

This can be summarised by stating that organisms have a shape, size and colour and have behaviour patterns that fit them best to their particular niche.

As an example, until our present environment changes, it is not possible to improve on sparrows, wild dogs, hawthorn or any other organism. They are all the best suited for the conditions.

The human impact

how the impact of human activity on the environment is related to population size, economic factors and industrial requirements;

At the moment, many humans expect an unrealistically high standard of living, and industries throughout the world often produce the goods in a careless way so there are serious problems for our planet.

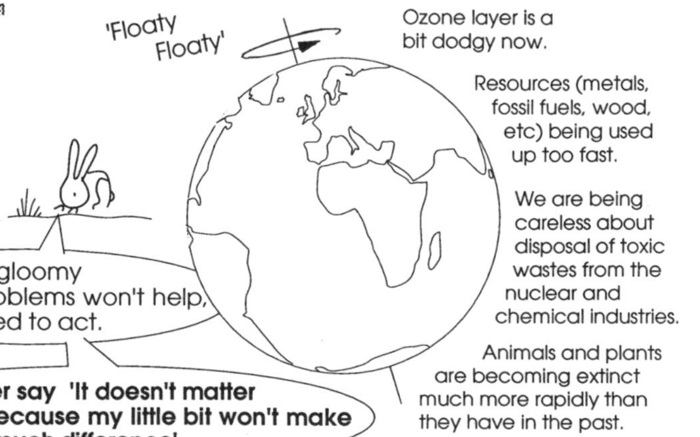

'Floaty Floaty'

Ozone layer is a bit dodgy now.

Resources (metals, fossil fuels, wood, etc) being used up too fast.

We are being careless about disposal of toxic wastes from the nuclear and chemical industries.

Being gloomy about the problems won't help, we need to act.

Animals and plants are becoming extinct much more rapidly than they have in the past.

Never say 'It doesn't matter what I do because my little bit won't make much difference'.

It is everybody's 'little bit' that has caused the problems we have now.

Here are some of the things that you can do as your contribution to reducing the damage.

1. Switch off the lights when they are not being used.
2. Don't waste water. It has to be pumped to your house which costs energy so take showers rather than baths and install a short-flush loo cistern when the old one wears out (or put an engineering brick in the cistern), don't leave the tap running while you brush your teeth.
3. Turn down your central heating by a degree or two (wear a few extra clothes instead)
4. Go to work by bike (it rains a great deal less than people think).
5. When there is a choice, choose products which have the least packaging around them.
6. Set up a separate bin for vegetable waste from the kitchen. If vegetable matter goes into the county waste tip it turns into methane. On your well-aerated compost heap it becomes CO_2, a much less damaging greenhouse gas (or even better! . . . put 15 cm of compost in your organic bin, add some vegetable waste and then put in some brindle worms from your local fishing tackle shop. The worms will keep converting vegetable matter to compost for the garden).
7. Start changing the way you think about what is important in life. This will be the hardest bit . . . We are now so tuned to thinking in terms of all our possessions that many of us even think of our partner as a possession. Damage to the environment and diminishing resources may force us to live a more simple, calm life. When this happens lots of people will discover again that real happiness comes from simple things like having friends you know really well, having people over for a meal or listening to music.

Our changing Earth

Major gradual changes in the Earth's climate do occur without any human action e.g. ice ages. But what worries us more at present are the changes we produce by our life styles e.g. rising CO_2 levels and global warming, increase in the sizes of many of the worlds deserts, rising levels of toxic waste which can contaminate land or water supplies now or in the future.

Desertification refers to the loss of productivity of the world's dry regions. It is affecting 250 million people in 5 continents and is being speeded up because the people there need to eat, cook and keep warm and so are forced to treat the land roughly. The main parts of this vicious circle are shown here.

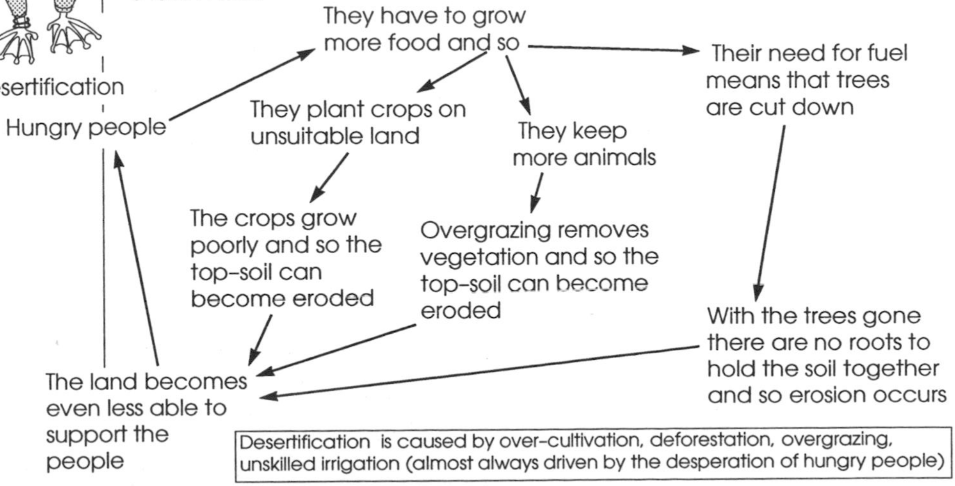

Desertification

Hungry people → They have to grow more food and so →

They have to grow more food and so → Their need for fuel means that trees are cut down

They plant crops on unsuitable land

They keep more animals

The crops grow poorly and so the top-soil can become eroded

Overgrazing removes vegetation and so the top-soil can become eroded

With the trees gone there are no roots to hold the soil together and so erosion occurs

The land becomes even less able to support the people

Desertification is caused by over-cultivation, deforestation, overgrazing, unskilled irrigation (almost always driven by the desperation of hungry people)

Living things in their environment | **adaptation and competition**

Natural springs	Industry operates on such a large scale now that vast amounts of waste are constantly produced. These must be stored somewhere, and careless disposal can contaminate the ground water. Bottled water is only as good as the spring that supplies the bottling plant.

a water pump getting water for the cattle or for bottling

industrial waste stored

natural spring

'putter'
'put'
'but'

a layer of clay, or other impermeable rock (e.g. shale)

nasty substances may be leaching into the ground water

This distance could be as much as 5000 km

Fossil fuels and the greenhouse effect (see also pages 72 & 73)	The greenhouse effect is a natural process – it has always been part of the Earth's atmospheric system – without it the average temperature at the surface would be –17°C. The problem arises from the enhancement of the greenhouse effect. Carbon, trapped in land plants has formed the main part of coal. Small water organisms have died and produced oil and natural gas. The carbon will be released as carbon dioxide when these chemicals are burned. Humans are burning fossil fuels on a vast scale and releasing huge amounts of carbon dioxide into the atmosphere. The rising levels of carbon dioxide and methane (released from the intestines of cattle, from the rich mud in paddy fields and from our refuse tips) are believed to be increasing the **Greenhouse Effect.** Carbon dioxide, methane and nitrogen oxides (NO_x) are believed to be preventing the heat that is reflected from the Earth's surface escaping into space. This results in a steady but slow rise in the Earth's temperature.
The Ozone layer	The **Holes in the Ozone Layer** have a different cause. The ozone in the upper atmosphere breaks down rapidly especially when chlorofluorocarbons (C F C s) and certain other chemicals are present. The C F C s are found in fridge coolants and many aerosol sprays. As the ozone layer shields us from much of the damaging ultra–violet rays arriving from the sun, destruction of this layer will mean that plants and animals all get larger doses of these rays. It may well result in an increase in the mutation rate in plants and cause an increase in skin cancer for us. We can reduce the risks of getting skin cancer or cataracts by wearing hats, shades and using UV blocker, we can't protect the plankton in the oceans or crops in the fields quite as easily.
Heavy metals	**Lead and cadmium** are released into the air from smelting works, or into the water from mining operations or from batteries carelessly thrown away and can accumulate in people's teeth, bones and kidneys (causing kidney damage and high blood pressure). Lead compounds are added to some petrols so that the vapour can withstand higher pressures before igniting i.e. it reduces the chances of 'knocking'. This allows the engines to give more power. Small children absorb lead more readily through the intestine than do adults, and it can pass into their nervous systems more easily.

The maximum permitted adult dose of lead is 6.5 µg/kg/day.
For children it is 1.2 µg/kg/day. Unfortunately, lead free petrol contains
benzene and this is very damaging to people (it is a cancer inducer).
Many heavy metals upset enzyme reactions and so can have a harmful
effect on living tissue.
(Water companies try to remove heavy metals from our drinking water.)

PCBs
Polychlorinated biphenyls have been blamed for causing the deaths of seals
in the North Sea by reducing their resistance to certain viruses. They are also
blamed for the increasing numbers of diseased fish brought up in the nets of
North Sea inshore fishermen.
Crude oil is being released into the sea by oil rigs, production platforms,
tanker captains washing out their oil tanks at sea (illegally), and by the
occasional foundering of loaded tankers. The most obvious and immediate
effect of this release is seen in the damage it does to sea birds. But crude oil
contains many highly toxic substances, and these are now washing about on
the sea bed in many parts of the world. Their effects may not become
noticeable for fifty years or more.

Herbicides
Dioxin, produced in small quantities during the manufacture of certain
herbicides (e.g. 2,4,5–T), can cause a severe form of acne, miscarriages,
tumours and cancers, as well as an increased incidence of mental handicap
in the children of parents who were exposed to dioxin. These effects have
been found in American and Vietnamese forests, and around the factories
at Seveso (Italy) and Bolsover (U.K.).

Insecticides
Organochlorine pesticides, like D D T , helped many people to rid their
countries of malaria mosquitoes, and so have been hugely beneficial but, at
the same time, have had very damaging effects on the environment. D D T,
for example, has caused massive reductions in the numbers of birds of prey
by affecting their fertility. These birds, living at the top of the food chain,
received the largest concentrations of the substances. These substances are
oil soluble and so are retained in the bodies of the first organisms in the food
chain. The oily substances are then taken in by organisms further up the food
chain and the damaging pesticides become increasingly concentrated until
eventually they reach toxic levels.

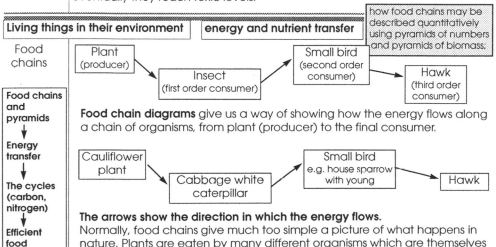

how food chains may be
described quantitatively
using pyramids of numbers
and pyramids of biomass;

Living things in their environment | **energy and nutrient transfer**

Food chains

| Plant (producer) | → | Insect (first order consumer) | → | Small bird (second order consumer) | → | Hawk (third order consumer) |

Food chain diagrams give us a way of showing how the energy flows along
a chain of organisms, from plant (producer) to the final consumer.

| Cauliflower plant | → | Cabbage white caterpillar | → | Small bird e.g. house sparrow with young | → | Hawk |

Food chains and pyramids
↓
Energy transfer
↓
The cycles (carbon, nitrogen)
↓
Efficient food production

The arrows show the direction in which the energy flows.
Normally, food chains give much too simple a picture of what happens in
nature. Plants are eaten by many different organisms which are themselves
the prey of several different carnivores. The **food web** is more realistic.

Living things in their environment | **energy and nutrient transfer**

Pyramids of numbers

These pyramids are diagrams which use boxes to represent the different groups of organisms (trophic levels) that act as channels for the energy from the sun. The energy comes ultimately from the sun and, eventually, it is all radiated back out to space.

Pyramid of numbers (example 1)

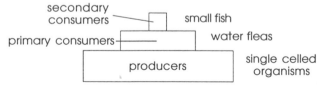

secondary consumers — small fish
primary consumers — water fleas
producers — single celled organisms

Pyramid of numbers (looking a bit wobbly)

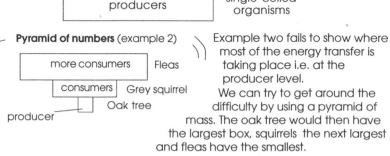

Pyramid of numbers (example 2)

more consumers — Fleas
consumers — Grey squirrel
producer — Oak tree

Example two fails to show where most of the energy transfer is taking place i.e. at the producer level.
We can try to get around the difficulty by using a pyramid of mass. The oak tree would then have the largest box, squirrels the next largest and fleas have the smallest.

Pyramid of mass

The size of the boxes represents the mass of the organisms at each level

another level of consumers — Fleas
consumers — Grey squirrel
producers — Oak tree

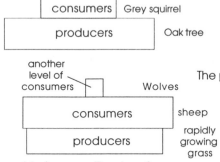

another level of consumers — Wolves
consumers — sheep
producers — rapidly growing grass

The pyramid on the left also fails to show where most of the energy transfer is taking place. Because the grass is being eaten as fast as it is growing the bottom box seems to be too small.

Pyramid of energy

Pyramid of energy The size of the boxes represents the rate of energy transfer through each level

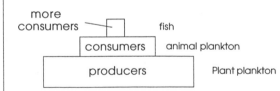

more consumers — fish
consumers — animal plankton
producers — Plant plankton

This way of presenting the results of surveys as an energy pyramid gives proper pyramids for every case investigated so far. (strangely though, knowledge of it is not required at Key Stage 4)

'0.02% for plants, 0.004% for herbivores, leaving only 0.0004% for creatures like me...Gosh! Not exactly a lot, is it?'

47% of the energy is used to heat up the earth

su

30% of the energy gets reflected back into space

23% is used to evaporate water which then forms clouds

about 0.2% drives the weather system

0.02% is absorbed by plants

For every 100 units of light energy that land on plants, about 50 are not of the correct wavelength to be absorbed by the chloroplasts and, because photo-synthesis is not completely efficient, only about 25% of the energy that lands on the plant is transferred to form carbohydrates.

An overall view which starts with the grass in the field.

69 % of the total is used by decomposers

17 % is eaten by other herbivores

9 % is lost as urine and faeces

4.4 % leaves as radiated heat or hot breath

0.6 % appears as the skin, bones, meat etc of the animal.

| Total energy produced in the animal's field i.e. 100% |
| The bullock gets about 14 % |

Now, let's consider how much of the animal's food appears as animal

how food production can be managed to improve the efficiency of energy transfer.

33 % is lost as heat and hot breath

63 % is lost in the faeces and urine

4 % appears as meat, bone, skin etc..

Let's make the total energy eaten by the animal be 100%

Improving the conversion rate

We can improve the conversion rate (grass to body mass) by keeping the animals indoors because :
1. The animals can be kept warm and so they use less of their food to keep themselves warm.
2. Being indoors, they will lose less energy moving about.
3. We bring their grass to them which means that less grass gets trampled or spoiled with faeces or urine.

Improving the conversion rate even more changing from eating warm-blooded animals like rabbits and cows to eating cold-blooded animals like trout.

			Percentage absorbed from food (%)	Percentage converted to body mass (%)
Warm blooded creatures i.e. homoiotherms	rabbit	50 %	2.6 %	Herbivores
	cow	37 %	4.1 %	
Cold-blooded creatures i.e. poikilotherms	trout	86 %	30.1 %	Carnivore
	grasshopper	91 %	13 %	Herbivore

- 50 -

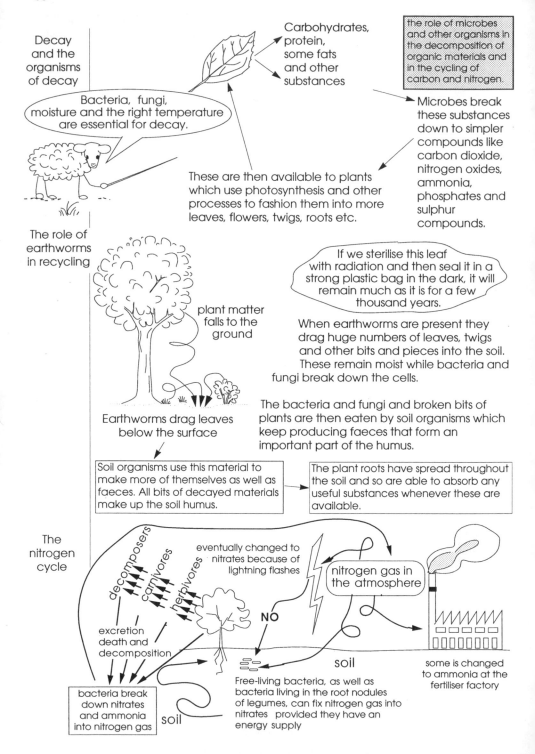

Decay and the organisms of decay

Carbohydrates, protein, some fats and other substances

the role of microbes and other organisms in the decomposition of organic materials and in the cycling of carbon and nitrogen.

Bacteria, fungi, moisture and the right temperature are essential for decay.

Microbes break these substances down to simpler compounds like carbon dioxide, nitrogen oxides, ammonia, phosphates and sulphur compounds.

These are then available to plants which use photosynthesis and other processes to fashion them into more leaves, flowers, twigs, roots etc.

The role of earthworms in recycling

plant matter falls to the ground

If we sterilise this leaf with radiation and then seal it in a strong plastic bag in the dark, it will remain much as it is for a few thousand years.

When earthworms are present they drag huge numbers of leaves, twigs and other bits and pieces into the soil. These remain moist while bacteria and fungi break down the cells.

Earthworms drag leaves below the surface

The bacteria and fungi and broken bits of plants are then eaten by soil organisms which keep producing faeces that form an important part of the humus.

Soil organisms use this material to make more of themselves as well as faeces. All bits of decayed materials make up the soil humus.

The plant roots have spread throughout the soil and so are able to absorb any useful substances whenever these are available.

The nitrogen cycle

decomposers carnivores herbivores

eventually changed to nitrates because of lightning flashes

nitrogen gas in the atmosphere

excretion death and decomposition

NO

soil

some is changed to ammonia at the fertiliser factory

bacteria break down nitrates and ammonia into nitrogen gas

soil

Free-living bacteria, as well as bacteria living in the root nodules of legumes, can fix nitrogen gas into nitrates provided they have an energy supply

Why bother with nitrogen ?

Nitrogen is an essential part of the substances that carry the genetic information, (**deoxyribonucleic acid** D N A), and of **proteins**, and so all plants and animals have nitrogen atoms as part of their structure.

Most organisms cannot use nitrogen gas directly. Plants have to absorb their nitrogen in the form of nitrates, ammonium salts or nitrites. Herbivores have to get their nitrogen by eating plants (e.g. as plant protein).

The concentration of nitrate in the soil will therefore be one of the factors that decides just how many organisms can inhabit a particular area.

The carbon cycle

When you think you know the nitrogen and carbon cycles, put the guide away and then try to write out your own. This way you quickly find the gaps in your knowledge.

fossil fuels burned on our behalf and carbon dioxide from natural sources

carbon dioxide

oxygen   plants

absorbed by the oceans and reacts with limestone

bacteria and fungi also produce carbon dioxide

oceans

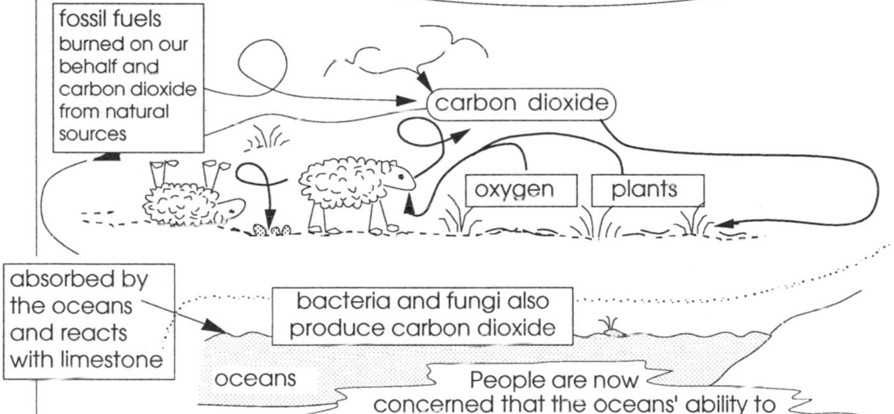

People are now concerned that the oceans' ability to absorb carbon dioxide has been pushed too far and that they will soon stop taking it up at the same rate.

It has been found that about 50% of the carbon dioxide produced by burning fossil fuels is absorbed by the oceans. These have played a very important part in slowing down the build-up of carbon dioxide in the atmosphere.

Have a look at pages 72 and 73 for another look at the carbon cycle.

K. S. 4 Materials and their Properties	Classifying materials

that solids, liquids and gases are all composed of particles;

atomic structure

Points to consider:
1. Matter is made of particles (atoms and molecules).
2. Between the particles there is nothing.
3. In solids the particles stay together because of forces of attraction.
4. If there were only forces of attraction the particles would get so close together that matter would be **very** dense.
5. Because this does not happen, we accept that when the particles get too close, repulsive forces become more effective than the forces of attraction, i.e a balance is reached. In solids the particles vibrate around these balance points.

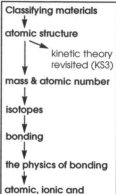

Topic flow chart

Classifying materials
↓
atomic structure → kinetic theory revisited (KS3)
↓
mass & atomic number
↓
isotopes
↓
bonding
↓
the physics of bonding
↓
atomic, ionic and molecular structures

The forces between the particles of the hammock strings are all that stop you from crashing to the ground.

The difference between solids, liquids and gases in terms of particles

The word **solid** covers materials from diamond (very hard) to rubber (quite flexible). Solids hold their shape if not acted on by forces. In a solid, the atoms and molecules are usually regularly arranged; they vibrate but don't move around.

Liquids flow into the shape of their containers. Unlike gases, they do not spread in all directions to fill the container because of the strong attractive forces between them. 'Spreadiness' can be an advantage because liquids will flow quite readily from the storage place to where they are being used, e.g. from petrol tank to car engine. In a liquid the atoms and molecules are close together. They slip over each other quite freely.

Gas particles spread out to fill their container. Because of this, they can be used as a squashy material, e.g. in pneumatic tyres. In a gas, the atoms / molecules have spread out quite a lot. They move in straight lines between collisions. There are almost no attractive forces between the particles.

Heating

As a substance heats up the particles in it vibrate or move more rapidly. These atoms and molecules are almost always on the move, either vibrating or whizzing about. They move in straight lines between collisions. There is nothing between the particles.

Cooling

As the solid cools down, the atoms and molecules vibrate more slowly. When they finally stop, that lump of matter has reached the lowest temperature that is possible for it: after all, you can't go any slower than stop! This lowest possible temperature is known as absolute zero, very close to $-273°$ C (0 on the Kelvin scale).

Pressure,

When particles bounce against each other, a force is produced. This force is spread over an area and we define pressure as the amount of force per area.

$$\text{Pressure} = \frac{\text{force}}{\text{area}} \quad \text{(the units are therefore newtons per metre}^2\text{)}$$

Diffusion

Whenever particles are free to move (as in a liquid or gas), the net effect is movement from regions of high to regions of low concentration. This movement takes place even though there are no draughts.
We call this movement diffusion. Diffusion is what causes the smell of perfume to spread through a room.

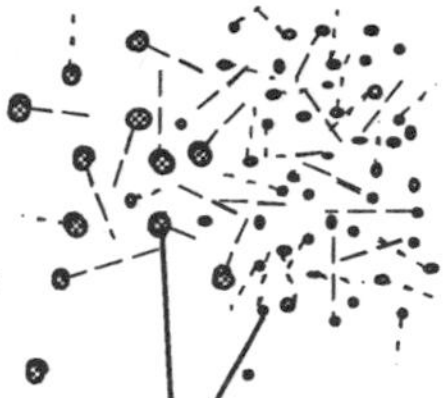

In the diagram on the right the large particles are concentrated on the left. These are moving more slowly.

Smaller and larger particles will gradually bounce their way into all the space available to them.

Melting and boiling

The turtle has just watched the boiling water in front of her, and is even now trying to figure out how energy can be absorbed without there being any change in temperature. Have a look at the graph below to see part of the answer to her ponderings. Whenever there is a **change in state** (solid to liquid or liquid to gas), the temperature does not change even though energy is given out or absorbed . The energy is needed just to free the particles from each other (melting) or to move them a lot further apart (evaporation).

Water

heat

Latent heat

Latent means 'hidden,' and the heat is 'hidden' because, although we keep adding energy, there is **no temperature change**. The energy is being used to cause a change of state i.e. change from solid to liquid or liquid to gas. Energy is released when the reverse changes (gas to liquid) occur.
Have a look at the plateaux on the graph.

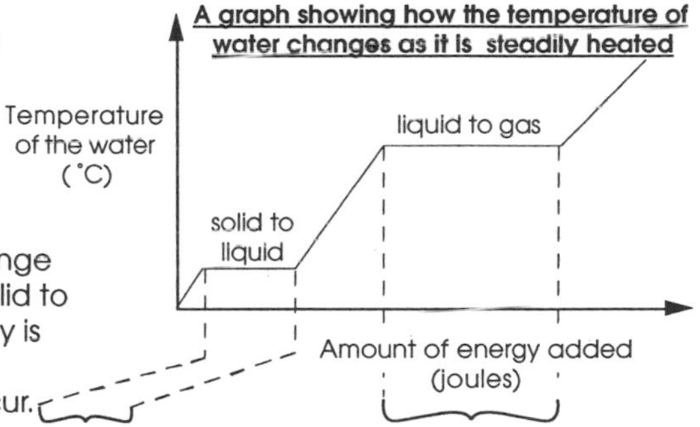

A graph showing how the temperature of water changes as it is steadily heated

Temperature of the water (°C)

liquid to gas

solid to liquid

Amount of energy added (joules)

This energy must be added just to get the ice to change to a liquid, i.e. to melt.

All this energy must be added just to get the water to change to a gas, i.e. to boil.

Atoms

Electrons and their arrangements

A diagram showing how the electrons and nucleus are arranged in the atom

that atoms consist of nuclei and electrons;

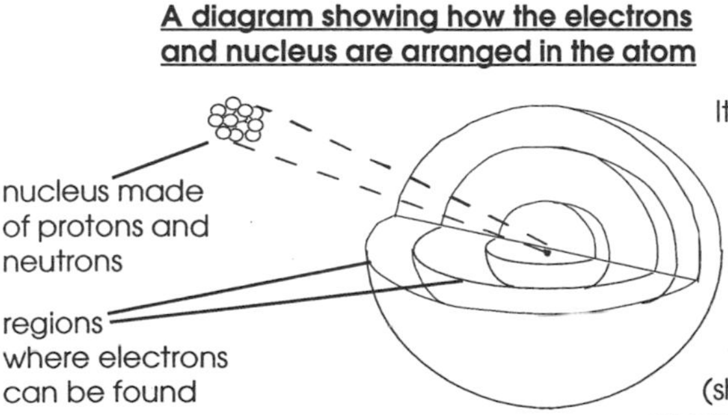

nucleus made of protons and neutrons

regions where electrons can be found

It is not correct to think of electrons as though they orbit the nucleus like planets around a star! Electrons tend to stick to certain regions. The picture shows three of these regions (shells). If you supply energy to the atom, the electrons jump from shell to shell getting further away from the nucleus. The electrons lose this energy by giving out electromagnetic radiation (light or other radiation) if they fall back towards the nucleus.

| K. S. 4 Materials and their Properties | Classifying materials | atomic structure |

Electrons, protons and neutrons are really tiny! If an atom of uranium were the size of an average bedroom, the nucleus would be the size of the full stop at the end of this sentence, and the 92 electrons would be thousands of times smaller. Between them there would be nothing, i.e. matter is mostly empty space!

More on atom structure

about a model of the way electrons are arranged in atoms;

All atoms are built of the same basic particles; **protons** and **neutrons** (in the nucleus) and **electrons** around the nucleus. For any neutral atom, the number of electrons equals the number of protons. The electrons are arranged in a series of shells around the nucleus. The first shell can hold two electrons and, when it is full, the electrons go into the next shell which can hold 8 electrons, and so on. If there are 8 electrons in the outermost shell, the element will be very stable ! Noble gases have 8 electrons in the outer shell.

Use the full periodic table while you are studying this, compare the two lots of information.

nucleus

first shell (can hold 2 electrons)

second shell (can hold 8 electrons)

third shell (can hold 18 electrons)

and there are more shells outside these

2 protons
2 neutrons
2 electrons

helium (He)

5 protons
6 neutrons
5 electrons

boron (B)

Atoms have three dimensions. We draw them flat because we need simple diagrams.

How electrons build up in the shells as atomic mass increases

If we put all the elements in order of increasing atomic mass and then go down the list, each new element will have one more proton and so have one more electron (than the previous element on the list) e.g. boron has 5 protons so carbon will have 6.

16 protons
16 neutrons
16 electrons

sulphur (S)

When we examine calcium we find that there are 8 electrons in the third shell (even though it can hold more) and 2 electrons in the fourth shell.

20 protons
20 neutrons
20 electrons

calcium (Ca)

Transition elements

Between calcium and gallium the third shell fills up with one electron for each new element, leaving two electrons in the outer fourth shell.

26 protons
30 neutrons
26 electrons

Use the information on this page and in the periodic table to draw your own diagram of an atom of bromine and krypton.

Iron (Fe)

Relative atomic mass	This is the mass of an atom compared to an atom of carbon 12. Carbon 12 is said to have a mass of 12. (There is no simpler way of saying this). Carbon 12 is the common form of carbon. The full term is 'relative atomic mass' 'relative' because all the masses are related to the mass of carbon 12.
Protons	Symbol: p Protons have much the same mass as a hydrogen atom (a hydrogen atom is composed of one proton and one electron). They are 1836 times heavier than an electron (having a mass of 6.673×10^{-27}kg). This last figure is not very helpful except for calculations as very few people can imagine 10^{-27}. A proton has a relative mass of one, and a single positive charge.
Neutron	Symbol: n The neutron also has a relative mass of one but carries no charge. (Neutrons can be split into an electron and a proton.) Neutrons are only stable when in the nucleus. Protons can exist outside the nucleus (e.g. a hydrogen ion is a proton).
Electron	Symbol: e$^-$ Electrons carry a single negative charge and have almost negligible mass. (an electron has about a 1836th of the mass of a proton)
Mass number	The mass number is the total number of protons and neutrons in the nucleus of each atom.
Atomic number	The atomic number of an element is the number of protons (+ charges) found in the nucleus of each atom. (Each proton carries a single positive charge.)
Isotopes	Isotopes are atoms that have the same chemical properties and therefore the same name and place on the periodic table , but they have different atomic masses. This difference is because the different atoms have the same number of protons but not the same number of neutrons.

(boxed notes: "the charges and relative masses of protons, neutrons and electrons;" and "about mass number, atomic number and isotopes;")

For example some chlorine atoms have 18 neutrons in the nucleus, others have 20 neutrons in each nucleus. The number of protons is the same (17) but atomic masses are different. We call these different atoms **isotopes** of chlorine. Their chemical properties will be identical but there will be very slight differences in their physical properties, e.g. melting point, boiling point, etc. Many atomic masses are not whole numbers e.g. Rb: 85.47. This is because such atomic masses are an average for the different isotopes that exist in nature.

A crude diagram of a $^{12}_{6}C$ A crude diagram of a $^{14}_{6}C$

The nucleus contains 6 protons and 6 neutrons

There are 6 electrons moving around the nucleus

The nucleus contains 6 protons and 8 neutrons

There are 6 electrons moving around the nucleus

The diagram is 'crude' for two reasons:
1. Atoms are 3-D structures.
2. The nucleus is tiny in comparison to the size of the atoms' outer boundaries.

Chemical reactions	Whenever elements react, the compounds that are produced during the reaction have some properties different to those of the elements from which they were formed.

that the reactions of elements depends on the arrangement of electrons in their atoms;

Example 1. Burning hydrogen in oxygen gives water which is very different from the gases that formed it.

that new substances are formed when atoms combine;

Example 2.

Sodium   +   Chlorine - - → POW - - - - Sodium chloride

very reactive metal !

Nasty, smelly gas !

"Yum, Yum !" (table salt)

Formation of ions	When the sodium and chlorine atoms collide, electrons jump from the sodium (metal) to the chlorine (non-metal). Electrons carry a negative charge and so the sodium becomes a positive ion and the chlorine atom becomes a negative ion (now called a chloride ion). Sodium chloride is an ionic compound.

about a model of the way electrons are arranged in atoms;

Chemistry involves the electrons in the outer shell of the reacting atoms and so we need to concentrate on these.

Some information on the alkali metals . . .	Consider the atoms of lithium, sodium and potassium. These have 3 electrons, 11 electrons and 19 electrons in their atoms respectively. **Similarities:** They each have a single electron in the outer shell i.e. they can contribute one electron in a reaction. This means that they will form ions with a single positive charge. **The difference:** As the atomic mass increases this single electron occupies a shell further away from the nucleus (i.e. the force from the nucleus that holds it in place gets weaker; the atom becomes more reactive) (therefore reactivity increases as we move down the group of alkali metals).

3 protons
3 neutrons
3 electrons
lithium (Li)

11 protons
12 neutrons
11 electrons
sodium (Na)

. . . and some on the halogens	Now we consider atoms of fluorine, chlorine and bromine. These have 9 electrons, 17 electrons and 35 electrons in their atoms respectively. **Similarities:** They each have seven electrons in the outer shell i.e. if they accept a single electron from some other atom, they will have 8 electrons in the outer shell. The outer shell will then become much more stable. This means that they will form ions with a single negative charge. **The difference:** Reactivity decreases as we move down the group from fluorine to astatine.

9 protons
10 neutrons
9 electrons
fluorine (F)

17 protons
18 neutrons
17 electrons
chlorine (Cl)

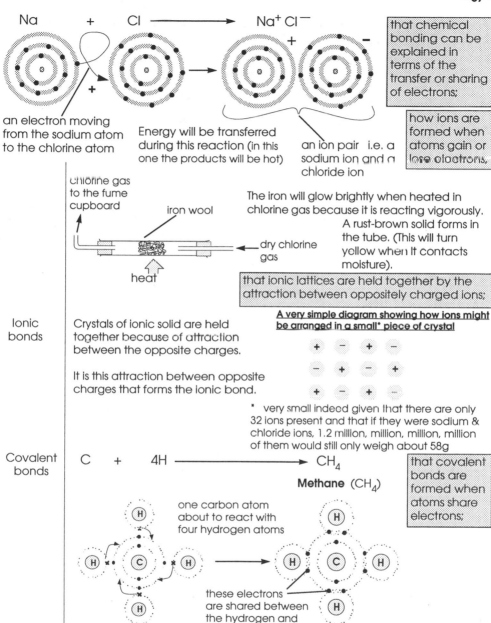

Na + Cl ⟶ Na^+ Cl^-

that chemical bonding can be explained in terms of the transfer or sharing of electrons;

an electron moving from the sodium atom to the chlorine atom

Energy will be transferred during this reaction (in this one the products will be hot)

an ion pair i.e. a sodium ion and a chloride ion

how ions are formed when atoms gain or lose electrons.

chlorine gas to the fume cupboard

iron wool

dry chlorine gas

heat

The iron will glow brightly when heated in chlorine gas because it is reacting vigorously. A rust-brown solid forms in the tube. (This will turn yellow when it contacts moisture).

that ionic lattices are held together by the attraction between oppositely charged ions;

Ionic bonds

Crystals of ionic solid are held together because of attraction between the opposite charges.

It is this attraction between opposite charges that forms the ionic bond.

A very simple diagram showing how ions might be arranged in a small* piece of crystal

```
+   −   +   −
  −   +   −   +
+   −   +   −
```

* very small indeed given that there are only 32 ions present and that if they were sodium & chloride ions, 1.2 million, million, million, million of them would still only weigh about 58g

Covalent bonds

C + 4H ⟶ CH_4

Methane (CH_4)

that covalent bonds are formed when atoms share electrons;

one carbon atom about to react with four hydrogen atoms

these electrons are shared between the hydrogen and carbon atoms (spending some time nearer one and some time nearer the other)

Covalent bond When atoms share some of their outer electrons, no atom has complete control of the shared electrons. There are no regions with strong positive or negative charge (like there are in ionic compounds).

Glucose, carbon dioxide and alcohol are examples of molecules in which the atoms are held together by covalent bonds.

Structure
of metals

Metallic bonds Crystals of metal are composed of positive metal ions held together by a sea of electrons. Some of the electrons are free to move but the metal ions are fixed into regular arrangements typical of crystals.

A force applied to one part of the crystal will cause the atom layers to slide over each other.
Sliding layers mean that metals can be bent or hammered into shapes (they are malleable) or drawn into wires (they are ductile).

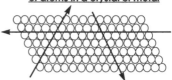

A diagram showing one arrangement of atoms in a crystal of metal

The arrows show three directions in which the layers will slide easily.

that substances with covalent bonds may form simple molecular structures or giant structures;

Giant
structures

Atoms and ions can pack together in a regular way in three dimensions to give a very large structure. The point about giant structures is that they have no obvious end.
A diamond (atomic giant structure) can be as big as the earth if you have enough carbon to build it that size and a high pressure oven big enough. There is no obvious point at which you stop building one diamond unit and begin on the next, but there is with water or glucose molecules.

Giant structures of non-metal atoms (e.g. sand and diamond) do not contain free electrons or ions (one exception is graphite which does contain free electrons and therefore will conduct as a solid).

I've put in a summary showing four ways that atoms join together to give the substances we see around us.

elements

react to form → simple molecules (joined by covalent bonding) e.g. the ethanoic acid in vinegar, glucose, amino acids, oxygen.

metals (metallic bonding to produce giant structures composed of atoms) e.g. crystals of zinc or iron.

giant structures of atoms (covalent bonding between the atoms) e.g. diamond, graphite.

react to form →

giant structure of ions e.g. many metal compounds (sodium chloride). These are made up of charged particles, ions, which conduct when they are free to move.

the physical properties of some substances with giant structures and some with simple molecular structures.

Some properties of metals

Physical properties of metals   They usually:

have high densities (not all though e.g. Na) — the atoms are closely packed

have high melting points and boiling points — they exist as giant structures

are good conductors of heat and electricity — there are free electrons drifting about between the atoms

are malleable and ductile. — the crystal structure is such that, although the forces between the atoms are strong, the layers are able to glide over each other

Some properties of the group of substances that include water, methane, olive oil, glucose, orthorhombic sulphur and iodine

Physical properties of non-metals with covalent molecules

they have low melting-points and boiling-points — the energy needed to separate the molecules is low. (There is weak bonding between molecules)

they do not conduct electricity in any state when pure — the electrons are too firmly held in the molecules

they are more soluble in solvents like cyclohexane than in water and the solutions do not conduct electricity. — the molecules do not carry a charge and so there is nothing for the positive or negative sides of the water molecules to bond with

Some care is needed here because there are many molecules e.g. water and glucose, that are not soluble in cyclohexane.

Some properties of the group of substances that have a giant ionic structure e.g sodium chloride, copper sulphate etc.

Physical properties of compounds with a giant ionic structure they:

have high melting points and boiling points — the bonds between the ions are strong and so a lot of energy is needed to separate the ions

are usually crystalline and the crystals can be cleaved — the ions pack together in a very regular way so that layers are formed

many are soluble in water — the ions carry positive or negative charges and so are readily surrounded by water molecules

do not conduct electricity when solid (but are good conductors when molten or in solution). — to conduct electricity the ions must be free to move and this only occurs when they are molten or in solution

Energy is needed to break bonds and energy is released during bond making.

	Type of bond	Bond energy
●—○	carbon–hydrogen bond	412 kJ mol^{-1}
●—●	carbon–carbon bond	348 kJ mol^{-1}
●—○	carbon–oxygen double bond	805 kJ mol^{-1}
○—○	hydrogen–oxygen bond	464 kJ mol^{-1}
○—○	oxygen–oxygen double bond	498 kJ mol^{-1}

Oil deposits

Points to note.

1. Most oil appears to have been formed in sedimentary rocks under the sea.
2. The oil has formed when great pressure and high temperatures (90° – 120°C) acted on the remains of plants or small marine organisms. (These remains have collected in huge deposits where little oxygen was present (i.e. under anaerobic conditions)).
3. Oil is rarely found in the place where it was formed because, being a low density liquid, it moves upwards through the rock.
4. It will continue to migrate upwards until it is trapped under an impervious layer e.g. a salt dome or dense cap rock, or has reached the surface (as in Trinidad where it has formed a lake of asphalt).
5. The oil deposit is not a lake of pure oil. It is a region of porous rock in which the pores are filled with oil, gas and water.
6. At these depths the rock is hot, and waxy substances are dissolved in the liquid oil. Once on the surface the oil cools and a lot of these substances settle out as solids.
7. Much of the oil in the reservoir will be forced to the surface by the gas under pressure.

drill string

Topic Flow Diagram

Oil deposits formation
↓
fractional distillation
↓
alkanes & alkenes
↓
cracking
↓
polymers

how oil deposits are formed;

Fractional distillation

A diagram showing the main features of a crude oil fractionation column

bubble caps

110°C

etc

crude oil in here

375°C

gas & gasoline
gasoline
naphtha
kerosene
gas oil
lubricants
fuel oil (for ships or boilers) and bitumen

that crude oil is a mixture of substances, most of which are hydrocarbons, which can be separated by fractional distillation;

The different substances present in crude oil can be separated by using fractional distillation.

Humans need lots of the smaller molecules for running their engines and for making plastics, and as a raw material in the chemistry industry, but as luck would have it, most crude oil contains more of the larger molecules (heavy oils, waxes and bitumen), than petrol and kerosene. (see cracking on page 62)

salt dome

gas

crude oil

cap rock
reservoir rock

Number of carbon atoms in the molecule	Description
1–4	Gas
4–10	Gasoline and Naphtha
10–16	Kerosene
16–20	Light gas oil
20–25	Heavy gas oil
>25	Reduced crude

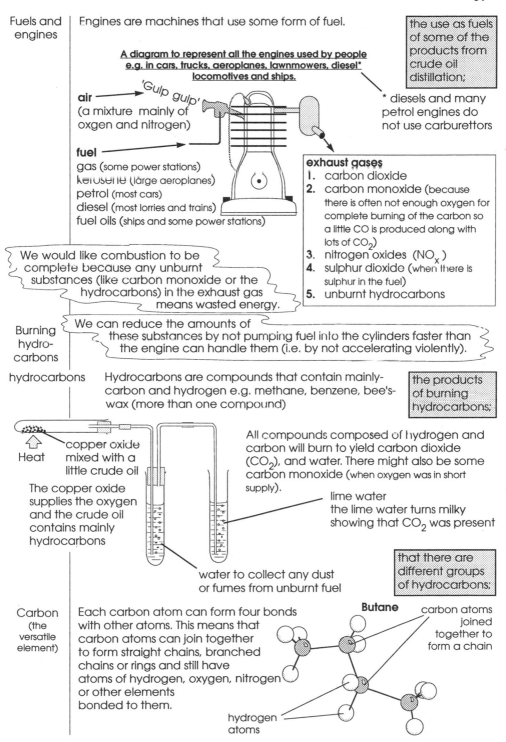

Fuels and engines

Engines are machines that use some form of fuel.

the use as fuels of some of the products from crude oil distillation;

A diagram to represent all the engines used by people e.g. in cars, trucks, aeroplanes, lawnmowers, diesel* locomotives and ships.

'Gulp gulp'

air ——
(a mixture mainly of oxgen and nitrogen)

fuel ——
gas (some power stations)
kerosene (large aeroplanes)
petrol (most cars)
diesel (most lorries and trains)
fuel oils (ships and some power stations)

* diesels and many petrol engines do not use carburettors

exhaust gases
1. carbon dioxide
2. carbon monoxide (because there is often not enough oxygen for complete burning of the carbon so a little CO is produced along with lots of CO_2)
3. nitrogen oxides (NO_x)
4. sulphur dioxide (when there is sulphur in the fuel)
5. unburnt hydrocarbons

We would like combustion to be complete because any unburnt substances (like carbon monoxide or the hydrocarbons) in the exhaust gas means wasted energy.

Burning hydro-carbons

We can reduce the amounts of these substances by not pumping fuel into the cylinders faster than the engine can handle them (i.e. by not accelerating violently).

hydrocarbons

Hydrocarbons are compounds that contain mainly-carbon and hydrogen e.g. methane, benzene, bee's-wax (more than one compound)

the products of burning hydrocarbons;

Heat
copper oxide mixed with a little crude oil

The copper oxide supplies the oxygen and the crude oil contains mainly hydrocarbons

All compounds composed of hydrogen and carbon will burn to yield carbon dioxide (CO_2), and water. There might also be some carbon monoxide (when oxygen was in short supply).

lime water
the lime water turns milky showing that CO_2 was present

that there are different groups of hydrocarbons;

water to collect any dust or fumes from unburnt fuel

Carbon
(the versatile element)

Each carbon atom can form four bonds with other atoms. This means that carbon atoms can join together to form straight chains, branched chains or rings and still have atoms of hydrogen, oxygen, nitrogen or other elements bonded to them.

Butane
carbon atoms joined together to form a chain

hydrogen atoms

Saturated and unsaturated compounds

A diagram showing two 5 carbon molecules, one which has single bonds and a second with double bonds

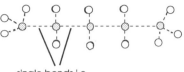

A saturated hydrocarbon

⊘ carbon atoms

○ hydrogen atoms

single bonds i.e. saturated bonds

An unsaturated hydrocarbon

double bonds i.e. unsaturated bonds

All the bonds on this page are covalent bonds

Note that each carbon is surrounded by four bonds.

Double bonds

Double bonds occur when atoms share two pairs of electrons. A double bond is stronger than a single bond with the same atoms. Substances containing double bonds are more reactive than those, like butane, with only single bonds.

that alkanes are saturated hydrocarbons, and alkenes are unsaturated hydrocarbons containing one double covalent bond between carbon atoms;

Alkanes (paraffins)

Propane

The alkanes contain only carbon and hydrogen and have their carbon atoms in chains held together by single bonds.

Number of carbons	Nature
1 to 4	gas
5 to 16	paraffin–like liquids
above 16	waxy solids

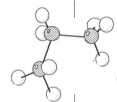

They are the main compounds found in crude oil. They burn in air to release energy, they produce carbon dioxide and water.

They do not react readily with most other substances but will form compounds with chlorine and bromine in the presence of bright light or UV. (The chlorine and bromine compounds are useful as solvents, as fire fighting liquids, as anaesthetics and as refrigerants).

The alkenes

The alkenes are chains of carbon and hydrogen which contain a double bond. Because of the double bond; they are much more reactive than the alkanes, their molecules can join together to make plastics, they will react with steam, with hydrogen, and with potassium permanganate. **Alkenes will remove the colour from bromine water** (because they react with the bromine to make a colourless compound). Alkanes won't do this in the dark.

Reactions with the halogens

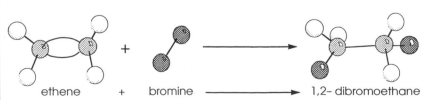

ethene   +   bromine ⟶ 1,2- dibromoethane

Reactions with hydrogen	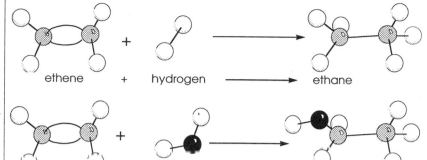

ethene + hydrogen ⟶ ethane

Reactions with water

ethene + water (as steam) ⟶ ethanol

Too much tar, too little petrol

Crude oil contains many different substances but not in the proportions that we consumers want them. Chemists have had to provide a way of 'cracking' the larger molecules in crude oil.

Cracking

We have worked out a way to **'crack'** (**catalytic cracking**) the larger molecules into the smaller molecules which burn more

> that hydrocarbon molecules can be cracked to form smaller molecules, including alkenes;

readily. We can also make petrol-sized molecules by joining (**alkylation**) gases. Both of these methods are used to get the required amounts of petrol for our modern societies.

If petrol is left for a while (like about 6 months)

> If I look angry it is because I have just spent 20 minutes on this mower trying to get it started. Pity I didn't think to change the petrol sooner!

'chug'
'chug'

the small molecules will join together forming larger molecules which burn and vaporise much less readily. This is often the reason why the lawn mower will not start very easily in the spring.

Polymers and their properties

Polythene

Synthetic polymers.

Polythene. Made by joining ethene molecules together into long chains (as many as 50 000 ethene units). It is useful because:

> that addition polymers can be made from alkenes formed during cracking;

1. It can be made into very thin strong films.
2. It is resistant to acid and alkali.
3. It won't rot.
4. It is a very good insulator.

> some uses of addition polymers;

Low density polythene has many little side branches on the long chains and so the chains will not pack closely together (hence 'low density'). It begins to soften as temperature rises toward 100°C.

High density polythene has chains without side branches and so the chains pack closely together (hence 'high density'). It is much more rigid and does not soften at 100°C.

Polythene	**Polythene** is one of the cheapest plastics and is used to make plastic bags, buckets, bowls and squeezy bottles (e.g. for washing up liquid), insulation on electric wiring etc.
Polyester	**Polyester.** Made as a polymer of certain alcohols (commonly glycol or propylene glycol). Polyesters are particularly good for making fibres used in clothes and as resins used in boat building.
Polystyrene	**Polystyrene.** Made by joining styrene molecules together and then be used to make foams, hamburger oyster packs, insulated disposable mugs, or used as fillers in paper or in the manufacture of paints.
Polyvinyl chloride (PVC)	**Polyvinyl chloride (PVC).** Made as a polymer of chloroethene (vinyl chloride). It is used for floor coverings, electrical coverings, toys, clothes, furnishings, packaging and luggage.
Natural polymers	**Natural polymers.** Polysaccharides. Polymers made by joining together sugar molecules into long chains, as happens in starch, glycogen, cellulose, pectin and the chitin fibres in insect cuticle. Polysaccharides are used as a store of energy (starch and glycogen), or as part of the structure (cellulose and chitin).
Polypeptides	Made by joining amino acids (see the bottom of page 10) to form long chains. In this case the name is taken from the type of bond (peptide bond) that joins the molecules together. Polypeptides are used in structures like bone, tendons, ligaments and used to make hair, finger nails, horns. They are also the working part of muscle and enzymes.
Lignin	This is a phenylpropene polymer. By combining with cellulose in wood it is responsible for the strength of the wood. It makes up 20 to 30 % of the mass of wood.
Rubber	Natural rubber is polyisoprene. It is not elastic when in the plant but may serve as an energy storage product and as a poisonous chemical which makes the plants less likely to be attacked by insects or other herbivores.
Nucleic acids	(The chemical that carries genetic information). These are very large molecules made from organic molecules joined together by sugar and phosphate groups.

useful products from metal ores and rocks — that metal ores are found in the Earth;

Metal ores	Most metals in rocks occur as compounds. Many occur in groups e.g. zinc is usually found together with lead.

Ten metals, the compound from which the metal is purified and the method used

Metal	Common ore and / or name of compounds	Method of extraction
Sodium	rock salt or brine, sodium chloride (NaCl)	electrolysis
Calcium	calcium chloride (CaCl$_2$)	electrolysis
Aluminium	bauxite, aluminium oxide (Al$_2$O$_3$)	electrolysis
Zinc	zinc blende, zinc sulphide (ZnS)	by heating with carbon
Iron	haematite, iron oxide (Fe$_2$O$_3$)	by heating with carbon
Lead	galena, lead sulphide (PbS)	by heating with carbon
Copper	copper pyrites, copper sulphide (CuS + FeS)	heated with limestone
Silver	as pure metal or as sulphide ores (Ag$_2$S)	various methods
Gold	as pure metal	various methods
Platinum	as pure metal	various methods

(in order of decreasing reactivity)

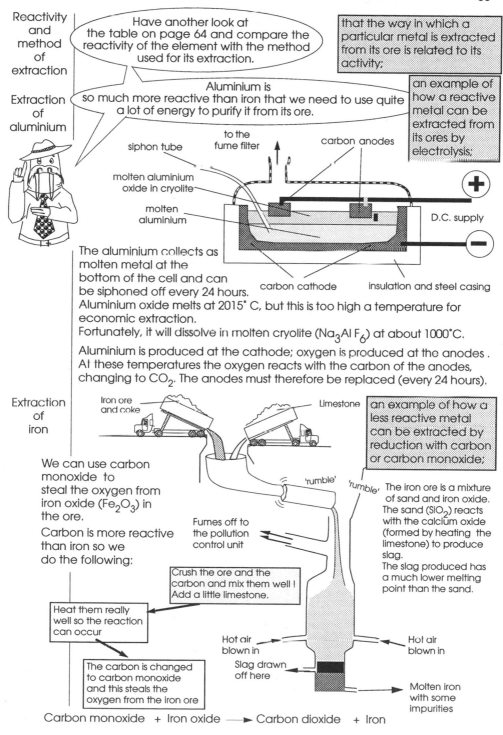

Reactivity and method of extraction

Have another look at the table on page 64 and compare the reactivity of the element with the method used for its extraction.

that the way in which a particular metal is extracted from its ore is related to its activity;

Extraction of aluminium

Aluminium is so much more reactive than iron that we need to use quite a lot of energy to purify it from its ore.

an example of how a reactive metal can be extracted from its ores by electrolysis;

to the fume filter

siphon tube

carbon anodes

molten aluminium oxide in cryolite

molten aluminium

D.C. supply

carbon cathode

insulation and steel casing

The aluminium collects as molten metal at the bottom of the cell and can be siphoned off every 24 hours.

Aluminium oxide melts at 2015° C, but this is too high a temperature for economic extraction.

Fortunately, it will dissolve in molten cryolite (Na_3AlF_6) at about 1000°C.

Aluminium is produced at the cathode; oxygen is produced at the anodes. At these temperatures the oxygen reacts with the carbon of the anodes, changing to CO_2. The anodes must therefore be replaced (every 24 hours).

Extraction of iron

Iron ore and coke

Limestone

an example of how a less reactive metal can be extracted by reduction with carbon or carbon monoxide;

We can use carbon monoxide to steal the oxygen from iron oxide (Fe_2O_3) in the ore.

Carbon is more reactive than iron so we do the following:

'rumble'

'rumble'

The iron ore is a mixture of sand and iron oxide. The sand (SiO_2) reacts with the calcium oxide (formed by heating the limestone) to produce slag. The slag produced has a much lower melting point than the sand.

Fumes off to the pollution control unit

Crush the ore and the carbon and mix them well ! Add a little limestone.

Heat them really well so the reaction can occur

The carbon is changed to carbon monoxide and this steals the oxygen from the iron ore

Hot air blown in

Hot air blown in

Slag drawn off here

Molten iron with some impurities

Carbon monoxide + Iron oxide ⟶ Carbon dioxide + Iron

useful products from metal ores and rocks

Extraction and purification of copper

Copper is a relatively unreactive metal and so it is fairly easily extracted from its ore.
Limestone and copper ore mixed and heated in a smaller version of the iron smelter (shown on the last page). After the slag is removed the molten copper is collected (it contains some iron sulphide, gold, silver and other metals). This metal is 98% to 99.5% pure copper.

an example of how a metal can be purified by electrolysis;

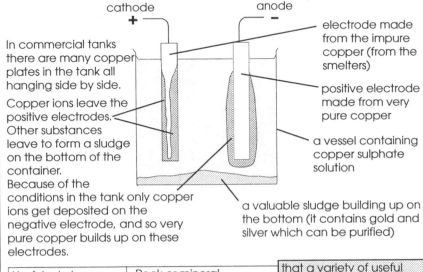

A diagram showing what is involved when copper is purified

cathode
+

anode
–

electrode made from the impure copper (from the smelters)

In commercial tanks there are many copper plates in the tank all hanging side by side.

positive electrode made from very pure copper

Copper ions leave the positive electrodes. Other substances leave to form a sludge on the bottom of the container.

a vessel containing copper sulphate solution

Because of the conditions in the tank only copper ions get deposited on the negative electrode, and so very pure copper builds up on these electrodes.

a valuable sludge building up on the bottom (it contains gold and silver which can be purified)

Useful substance	Rock or mineral
metals	various metal ores
calcium carbonate	limestone or chalk
sulphur	deposits of sulphur
building materials	stone, ingredients for cement
clay for pottery	china clay or the more usual clay

that a variety of useful substances can be made from rocks and minerals;

useful products from air

Producing ammonia

Fritz Haber

Ammonia is very important to our way of life in the 20th century. We use it to make fertilisers, nylon, nitric acid (which is used in many other processes) and for wood pulp production.
Almost all our nitrogen is produced by a process first developed by Fritz Haber in the early part of this century.

how nitrogen can be converted to ammonia in industry;

$$N_2(g) \quad + \quad 3H_2(g) \rightleftharpoons 2NH_3(g)$$

The combination of nitrogen and hydrogen takes place provided the pressure is kept between 150 - 300 atmospheres and the temperature is in the region 350° C- 450°C and the right catalysts are present. (Obviously this is a process not totally without danger.)

wood pulp production
nitric acid
nylon
fertilisers

A diagram showing the sequence involved in making ammonia from nitrogen and hydrogen (the Haber process)

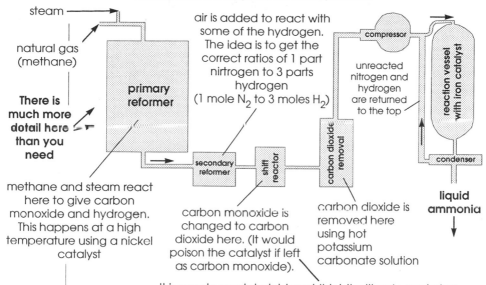

steam ⟶

natural gas (methane)

There is much more detail here than you need

primary reformer

air is added to react with some of the hydrogen. The idea is to get the correct ratios of 1 part nitrogen to 3 parts hydrogen (1 mole N_2 to 3 moles H_2)

compressor

unreacted nitrogen and hydrogen are returned to the top

reaction vessel with iron catalyst

secondary reformer

shift reactor

carbon dioxide removal

condenser

liquid ammonia ↓

methane and steam react here to give carbon monoxide and hydrogen. This happens at a high temperature using a nickel catalyst

carbon monoxide is changed to carbon dioxide here. (It would poison the catalyst if left as carbon monoxide).

carbon dioxide is removed here using hot potassium carbonate solution

It is easy to read straight past this bit without wondering how the chemists have managed a system that oxidises carbon monoxide without affecting the hydrogen.

Fertilisers

Nitrogen fertilisers are usually nitrates or ammonium salts. Ammonium nitrate is produced from ammonia gas and nitric acid, and contains 35% nitrogen in a form that plants can take up and use. It is the most widely used fertiliser.

how nitrogenous fertilisers are manufactured, and their effects on plant growth and the environment;

Nitro-chalk consists of ammonium nitrate crystals coated with calcium carbonate. The calcium carbonate will serve to neutralise the soil. Plants do not take up nutrients well if the soil is too acidic.
See page 33 for details of plants using fertilisers.

A section through a wheat field showing the land drains

Fertiliser run-off

Some of the fertiliser applied to fields is washed down beyond the reach of the roots of the crop plants. It then either continues to be washed down to the ground water or the nutrient rich water gets into the field drains and runs off into the local river system. More fertile water in the rivers will allow weeds and algae to grow rapidly so that the water becomes murky or overgrown with weeds. Bacteria multiply and lower the oxygen levels

Frost action

Soil grains, exposed to frosts, crack and release some of the substances trapped inside. This can be an important source of potassium salts.

rain water with dissolved fertilisers

land drain made from perforated plastic (or pottery) pipe buried in the soil (below ploughing level)

Ammonium ions and Ammonia

Ammonia is composed of molecules and exists as a gas at room temperature (NH_3).
Ammonium is the term used for the ion (NH_4^+) as in ammonium nitrate.

Qualitative An assessment of amount or size (or extent) which does not use figures. It deals just with qualities like tall or short or 'it has been very dry lately' ! 'there were lots of people at the meeting'. etc.

Quantitative In this case we are concerned with quantities, i.e. actual numerical values like 2.13m or 1.25cm or the 22753 people at the meeting.

Use of symbols and formulae for atoms, molecules and ions. In order to save time when writing out reactions, chemists have devised a shorthand for themselves. The rules are fairly simple.

to represent reactions, including electrolytic reactions, by balanced equations using chemical symbols;

The numbers of atoms, and groups of atoms, in each compound formula are indicated in a specific way:

$NaCl$ KNO_3 $CuSO_4$ $Cu(NO_3)_2$ $3Cu(NO_3)_2$

one sodium
one chlorine

one potassium
one nitrogen
three oxygens
i.e. one nitrate

one copper
one sulphur
four oxygen

one copper
two nitrates

three copper nitrates

sodium hydroxide + sulphuric acid ⟶ sodium sulphate + water

$2 NaOH (s)$ + $H_2SO_4 (aq)$ ⟶ $Na_2SO_4(aq)$ + $H_2O(l)$

solid   solution in water (aqueous)   liquid

There is very little magic involved in chemistry. You should always get out what you put in! Bit like life . . . really.

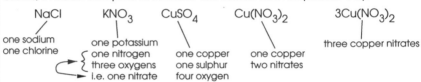

$2Na + 1S + 6O + 4H$ $2Na + 1S + 6O + 4H$

An exact balance

The shorthand for ions is pretty obvious really. The positive charges on metals ions are shown as '+'.
The negative charges on most non-metal ions are shown as – .
Thus: Copper ion = Cu^{2+} Sodium ion = Na^+

Conservation of mass in reactions In a reaction, the total mass of chemicals before (reactants) equals the total mass of chemicals after (products). If gases are formed, these must be weighed as well, or the mass afterwards will be smaller than expected.

Some general reactions

metal carbonates + acids ⟶ salt + carbon dioxide + water
$MgCO_3$ + H_2SO_4 ⟶ $MgSO_4$ + CO_2 + H_2O

metal hydroxides + acids ⟶ salt + water
$NaOH$ + HCl ⟶ $NaCl$ + H_2O

metal oxides + acids ⟶ salt + water
CuO + H_2SO_4 ⟶ $CuSO_4$ + H_2O

(continued)

A few more general reactions

$$\text{metal} \quad + \quad \text{acids} \longrightarrow \text{salt} \quad + \quad \text{hydrogen}$$
$$\text{Zn} \quad + \quad 2HNO_3 \longrightarrow Zn(NO_3)_2 + \quad H_2$$

$$\text{food molecules} \quad + \quad \text{oxygen} \longrightarrow \text{carbon dioxide} \quad + \quad \text{water}$$
e.g. carbohydrate, fat etc.

$$C_6H_{12}O_6 \text{ (glucose)} + \quad 6O_2 \longrightarrow \quad 6CO_2 \quad + \quad 6H_2O$$

Balancing equations

Ionic equations

When balancing equations, remember that you are not allowed to invent any new substances. If for example, you are dealing with zinc carbonate $ZnCO_3$, and you need to have 2 carbons to balance your equation, you mustn't cheat by inventing the new substance with two carbons in the carbonate.

If we look closely at reactions we can often see that some of the ions present are not involved in the reaction itself.

If you need to have two carbons then add two zinc carbonates and go back to the left side of the equation and correct the numbers of zinc and oxygen on that side.

They start as ions and at the end they are still the same ions . . they have just been spectators.

Sometimes you have to change things back and forth a few times before you get it right.

Step–by–step writing of an ionic equation

1. Write out the equation leaving space for additions.

$$\text{metal hydroxides} \quad + \quad \text{acids} \longrightarrow \text{salt} \quad + \quad \text{water}$$
$$NaOH \quad + \quad HCl \longrightarrow NaCl \quad + \quad H_2O$$

2. Add the states e.g. solid(s), liquid(l), gas(g) or aqueous solution(aq).

$$\text{metal hydroxides} \quad + \quad \text{acids} \longrightarrow \text{salt} \quad + \quad \text{water}$$
$$NaOH_{(aq)} \quad + \quad HCl_{(aq)} \longrightarrow NaCl_{(aq)} + \quad H_2O_{(l)}$$

Write out all the ions and then cancel those present on both sides of the equation

$$Na^+_{(aq)} + OH^-_{(aq)} + H^+_{(aq)} + Cl^-_{(aq)} \longrightarrow Na^+_{(aq)} + Cl^-_{(aq)} + H_2O_{(l)}$$

The ionic equation

$$OH^-_{(aq)} \quad + \quad H^+_{(aq)} \longrightarrow H_2O_{(l)}$$

Reactions during electrolysis

During electrolysis electrons combine with cations and are removed from anions.

We can write equations for the reactions taking place at the electrodes during electrolysis of molten zinc chloride as follows:

At the cathode

two electrons

$$Zn^{2+}_{(aq)} \quad + \quad 2e^- \longrightarrow Zn_{(s)}$$

At the anode

$$2Cl^-_{(aq)} \longrightarrow Cl_{2(g)} \quad + \quad 2e^-$$

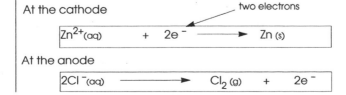

| K. S. 4 Materials and their Properties | Changing materials | quantitative chemistry |

The mole — This is the quantity of substance that contains 6.023×10^{23} molecules, atoms or ions. (A more formal definition involves the same number of particles as there are in 12 g of $^{12}_{6}C$. If we weigh out the RAM of an element in grammes, we have a mole of atoms of that element, e.g. a mole of sulphur weighs 32.064 g i.e. 32 g).

Atomic mass — First, some examples:

> **hydrogen atom**   approximately **1** atomic mass unit (amu)
> **carbon atom**   exactly **12** (a.m.u.)
> **nitrogen atom**   approximately **14** (a.m.u.)

An explanation. As we would expect, the atoms of the different elements have different masses. When comparing atoms, scientists have devised a workable system by letting a carbon atom have a mass of 12 atomic mass units. Atoms of other elements are then compared to the carbon 12 atom.

Relative molecular mass — To get the relative molecular mass (or formula mass in any general case), just add up all the separate atomic masses in the compound's formula, e.g :

$$Cu\,SO_4$$

one copper (64) + one sulphur (32) + four oxygens (4 x 16) = 160

The formula mass of anhydrous copper sulphate is 160 a.m.u.

When we investigate chemical reactions, the numbers of atoms involved are important.   (atomic mass units)

We can use the relative atomic masses to help us here.
12g. of carbon contains 6×10^{23} atoms of carbon.
1g. of hydrogen contains 6×10^{23} atoms of hydrogen.
This pattern holds for all atomic masses and formula masses.
These masses are useful in chemistry and so they have been given a name.
A mole is the amount of substance that contains the same number of atoms as there are in 12 g. of carbon–12.

$$\text{number of moles} = \frac{\text{mass of substance}}{\text{relative atomic mass*}}$$

*or formula mass

$24\ dm^3$ of any gas at room temperature and pressure contains 6×10^{23} <u>particles</u>

(It is important to remember that the noble gases, helium, neon etc. exist as atoms, while the other gases occur as molecules)

Hi Folks!
I have included a set of graded examples for you to look at.

to use chemical equations to predict reacting quantities;

Worked Examples

1.   What is the formula mass of potassium nitrate ?

| 1. First write down the chemical formula | ⟶ $K\,NO_3$ |

| 2. Look up the atomic mass of each atom in the formula | $39 + 14 + (16 \times 3)$ |

| 3. Add them together | ⟶ total = 101 |

2. What is the mass of 0.3 Moles of Fe Cl$_3$?

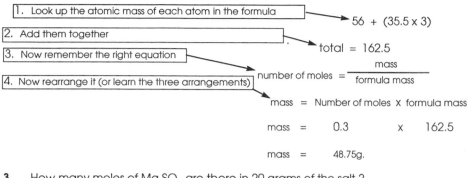

1. Look up the atomic mass of each atom in the formula

2. Add them together

3. Now remember the right equation

4. Now rearrange it (or learn the three arrangements)

$$56 + (35.5 \times 3)$$

$$total = 162.5$$

$$number\ of\ moles = \frac{mass}{formula\ mass}$$

$$mass = Number\ of\ moles \times formula\ mass$$

$$mass = 0.3 \times 162.5$$

$$mass = 48.75g.$$

3. How many moles of Mg SO$_4$ are there in 20 grams of the salt ?

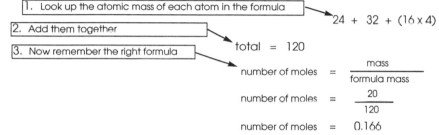

1. Look up the atomic mass of each atom in the formula

2. Add them together

3. Now remember the right formula

$$24 + 32 + (16 \times 4)$$

$$total = 120$$

$$number\ of\ moles = \frac{mass}{formula\ mass}$$

$$number\ of\ moles = \frac{20}{120}$$

$$number\ of\ moles = 0.166$$

4. 6 grams of magnesium are reacted with excess hydrochloric acid and the hydrogen gas produced is collected;   (RAM Mg = 24)

$$Mg + 2HCl \longrightarrow MgCl_2 + H_2$$

a. How many moles of magnesium are reacted in the experiment ?

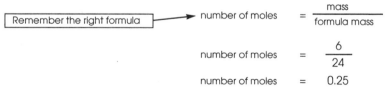

Remember the right formula

$$number\ of\ moles = \frac{mass}{formula\ mass}$$

$$number\ of\ moles = \frac{6}{24}$$

$$number\ of\ moles = 0.25$$

b. What mass of magnesium chloride will be produced in the reaction ?

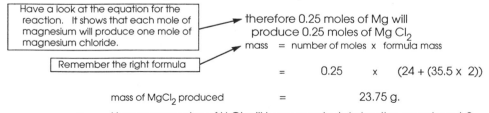

Have a look at the equation for the reaction. It shows that each mole of magnesium will produce one mole of magnesium chloride.

Remember the right formula

therefore 0.25 moles of Mg will produce 0.25 moles of Mg Cl$_2$

$$mass = number\ of\ moles \times formula\ mass$$

$$= 0.25 \times (24 + (35.5 \times 2))$$

$$mass\ of\ MgCl_2\ produced = 23.75\ g.$$

c. How many moles of H Cl will have reacted during the experiment ?

Have another look at the equation and we see that one mole of magnesium will react with 2 moles of H Cl

Therefore 0.25 moles of magnesium will have reacted with 0.5 moles of H Cl

K. S. 4 Materials and their Properties | **Changing materials** | **changes to the atmosphere**

It is generally believed that the young Earth was a very different place to the one we know today. I've listed the ways in which its atmosphere may have been different.

how the atmosphere and oceans evolved to their present composition;

I say 'may have been' because not all scientists are convinced that the early atmosphere had no free oxygen.

Early atmosphere

The Earth was cooling down from about 8000°C.

As it cooled, carbon and metals settled out to form the Earth's core.

There was very little free oxygen, the oxygen had combined to form oxides with carbon and other elements e.g. metals.

The atmosphere may have been composed mainly of carbon dioxide, water vapour, ammonia, methane with other gases.

There was no ozone layer to block incoming UV but other gases e.g. methane, are quite good UV blockers.

The changing atmosphere

As time passed, the oxygen levels rose and the carbon dioxide levels fell (once plants had appeared they began to change the carbon dioxide to oxygen and plant matter).

The ammonia would steadily be used to produce protein in plants.

Even though methane is only reactive at high temperatures the methane would be slowly oxidised to carbon dioxide and water.

$$CH_4 + 2O_2 \longrightarrow CO_2 + 2H_2O$$

Our atmosphere

Gas	Volume %
nitrogen	78
oxygen	21
argon	1
carbon dioxide	0.03

N.B. have a look at the top of page 73 for detail on the forests

how the carbon cycle helps to maintain atmospheric composition;

The carbon cycle revisited (have another look at page 51)

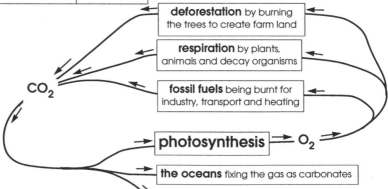

CO_2

deforestation by burning the trees to create farm land

respiration by plants, animals and decay organisms

fossil fuels being burnt for industry, transport and heating

photosynthesis → O_2

the oceans fixing the gas as carbonates

limestone and chalk areas like the vast highlands of Tibet and Nepal or the limestone areas of middle Europe and elsewhere. The limestone dissolves (slowly) in carbonic acid (rain with CO_2) and is carried away by rivers

$$CaCO_3 + H_2CO_3 \rightleftharpoons Ca(HCO_3)_2$$

calcium carbonate + carbon dioxide + water $\rightleftharpoons$ calcium hydrogen carbonate

| Forests and global warming | If coal beds are being laid down below forest then such forests are taking CO_2 out of the air and putting the carbon part away in the ground. Tropical forests have very little organic matter in the soil. There is very rapid recycling of nutrients and carbon. **We can say therefore that tropical forests are not important as sinks for CO_2.** They do have an important effect on regional weather and, if they are burnt to make space for farms, then the wood turns to CO_2 and adds to the atmospheric load of this gas. (If the trees are cut down and turned into furniture which is then kept for centuries, the effect on the atmosphere will be much less). Organic matter is being laid down in the peat bogs of northern Russia, Europe and Canada and these peat bogs act as a sink for CO_2. |

| Factors that tend to unsettle our atmosphere | Burning fossil fuels (peat, coal, oil, natural gas) releases huge amounts of carbon dioxide. Increasing population size has meant that more land must be used for food and more animals must be kept. Rice paddy fields and cattle are major producers of methane. Industrial and other activity (e.g. humans making plastics, cleaning ovens, spraying their hair) releases many organic solvents into the air. Volcanoes release sulphuric acid, sulphur dioxide, methane and dust when they erupt. |

| Factors maintaining the steady state | Plants are taking up carbon dioxide and producing a steady supply of oxygen during photosynthesis. Animals are taking up oxygen and producing carbon dioxide. The oceans are very important because they have been taking up (as carbonates) much of the carbon dioxide released when we burn fossil fuels. |

geological changes;

A diagram showing a region of Lesotho 160 million years ago
at the time of the breakup of Gondwanaland

| The formation of rocks

Igneous rock | extruded basalt

A basalt layer on the surface of Lesotho. It was formed when magma flowed up onto the surface through layers of sandstone. The basalt is relatively soft and so has worn away, leaving the huge sandstone-lined valley. A later intrusion of harder rock occurred where the waterfall is today.

All this activity took place because of the stresses induced when the continents first began to move. The magma in this region of Africa was very fluid and so flowed a long way out over the surface. |

please look on page 74 for the KS4 details

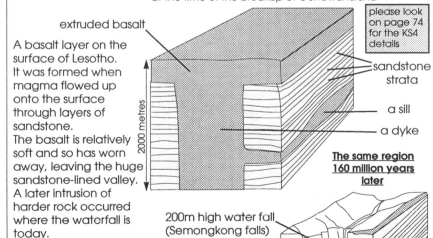

sandstone strata

a sill

a dyke

The same region 160 million years later

2000 metres

200m high water fall (Semongkong falls)

| K. S. 4 Materials and their Properties | Changing materials | geological changes |

Sedimentary rocks

The sandstone deposits under the mountains of Lesotho extend a long way out into the neighbouring country (South Africa).
They were laid down at a time when that part of the world was a huge, flat steppe -like plain with scattered marshes.

how igneous rocks are formed by the cooling of magma, sedimentary rocks by the deposition and consolidation of sediments, and metamorphic rocks by the action of heat and pressure on existing rocks;

This is given as an example of the scale and variety of sedimentary rocks.

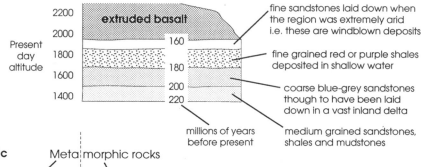

A section through part of Lesotho showing the arrangement of sandstones overlaid with basalt

fine sandstones laid down when the region was extremely arid i.e. these are windblown deposits

fine grained red or purple shales deposited in shallow water

coarse blue-grey sandstones though to have been laid down in a vast inland delta

medium grained sandstones, shales and mudstones

Metamorphic rocks

Meta¦morphic rocks

changed   form

Rocks, being the rugged tough structures that most of them are, need high pressures and / or temperatures to bring about significant changes.

We find these sorts of temperatures and pressures all along the edges of large intrusions of igneous rock, or in regions where 'bubbles of heat' rise up through the crust (as happens below the Rockies above the subduction zone (see page 76 for details of subduction zones).

A summary

Sedimentary rocks are formed from sediments (on river, sea or lake beds as well as on alluvial plains).
They can be very hard (limestone and flint), or fairly soft like shale.
They often contain fossils.

Igneous rocks When molten material is forced up to the surface (or cools just below the surface) by pressure from below, it solidifies and forms igneous rocks. Acid igneous rocks contain a great deal of silica and will break down to make acid soils. Other igneous rocks may be alkaline.

Metamorphic rocks have had their properties changed by heat , pressure and chemical action. Metamorphic rocks can be formed from any of the rock types.

Original rock	Metamorphic rock
sedimentary ⎧ Shale	→ Slate
⎩ Limestone	→ Marble
igneous — Granite	→ Gneiss

Plate tectonics | Evidence is steadily mounting to support the idea that the continents are large blocks of rock floating on the magma and moving slowly about the Earth's surface. When the first maps of the world were produced, in about 1550, people noticed that certain of the continents' shapes fitted together well.

how plate tectonic processes are involved in the formation, deformation and recycling of rocks.

The continents on the right (plus Australia) are believed to have been part of Gondwanaland about 200 million years ago.
The idea is that the Earth's crust is composed of plates (tectonic plates) with spectacular activity taking place at the margins of the plates.
There are 7 major plates and 12 smaller ones. The plate margins are divided into three types:

Gondwanaland

Africa

India

South America

South Pole

1. **Constructive,** where new ocean floor is being added at a mid-ocean ridge.

2. **Destructive,** where the moving ocean floor is forced down towards the mantle by pushing against a continent (at a subduction zone).

3. A **neutral zone** where the plates slide against each other sideways.

Eur-Asian plate

American plate

Pacific plate

Nazca plate

African plate

Antarctic plate

Constructive margin | Rising molten rock meets the crust and spreads out sideways, producing large forces which move the ocean floor apart. The molten rock solidifies on contact with the water (forming pillow lava) and becomes part of the ocean floor. This process is going on even as you read this.

There is good evidence for this as cameras have observed the volcanic activity in many deep ocean trenches.

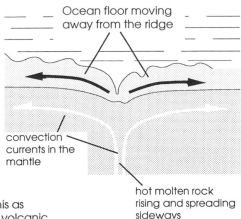

Ocean floor moving away from the ridge

convection currents in the mantle

hot molten rock rising and spreading sideways

K. S. 4 Materials and their Properties | **Changing materials** | **geological changes**

Subduction zones

The crust, which was part of the ocean floor, with its layer of sediment is 'diving' down at the edge of the continent.

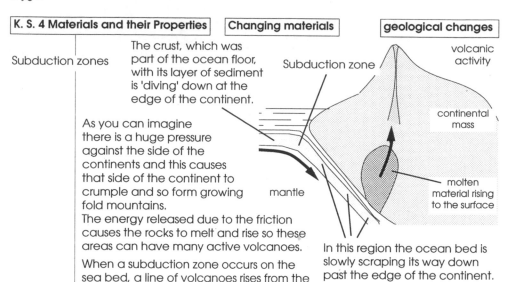

As you can imagine there is a huge pressure against the side of the continents and this causes that side of the continent to crumple and so form growing fold mountains.

The energy released due to the friction causes the rocks to melt and rise so these areas can have many active volcanoes.

When a subduction zone occurs on the sea bed, a line of volcanoes rises from the ocean floor eventually forming a chain of islands

In this region the ocean bed is slowly scraping its way down past the edge of the continent. Vast amounts of energy are being released due to friction.

Mountain building

Andes

Himalayas

Hawaii

There are five main ways in which mountains can appear.
1. Sideways pressure on the crust at a subduction zone can cause the crust to fold and crumple. This gives long chains of mountains like the Rockies or Andes.
2. Sideways pressure on the crust; because two land masses have 'collided' as they drifted across the Earth's surface. This is believed to be the process involved in the formation of the Himalayas in Tibet, Nepal and other nearby regions in Asia.
3. Direct uplift of continental rocks (not because of crumpling following sideways forces), but due to movements within the mantle.
4. Volcanic activity in which the mountain is built up from the material thrown out by the volcano. Many of the pacific islands (e.g. Hawaii) and mountains like St Helens in the Rockies are examples of this type.
5. Mountains can also be formed because they are left behind after the surrounding softer rock has been eroded away over millions of years. Such mountains often have a layer of harder rock at the top protecting the layers below from the worst of the erosion.

The rock cycle

Weathering → Erosion → Transportation → Deposition → Subsidence → Volcanic activity or metamorphic changes may occur here → Uplift → Weathering

The oceans (then and now)

Rivers carry dissolved substances (e.g. salts leached from the soil)down to the seas. Water evaporates from the sea and returns as fresh water to the land. Over the years since the beginning of the Earth as a planet, this process has resulted in the sea water becoming steadily more concentrated.

| **the periodic table** |
| Mendeleev |
| The table |
| Periods |
| Groups |
| Metals and non-metals |
| The main physical differences between metals and non-metals |

Transition metals (vertical label alongside Sc–Zn)

Transition metals (vertical label alongside Y–Cd)

Element column: H, He, Li, Be, B, C, N, O, F, Ne, **Na**, Mg, Al, Si, P, S, Cl, Ar, **K**, Ca, Sc, Ti, V, Cr, Mn, Fe, Co, Ni, Cu, Zn, Ga, Ge, As, Se, Br, Kr, **Rb**, Sr, Y, Zr, Nb, Mo, Tc, Ru, Rh, Pd, Ag, Cd, In, Sn, Sb, Te, I, Xe, **Cs**

In the last century there were several attempts to organise the elements into a table.

that the periodic table shows all elements, arranged in order of ascending atomic number;

Mendeleev (1869) set out the table which is pretty much what we use today. His table was good because:

1. He realised that it needed gaps for those elements that hadn't yet been discovered.
2. He suggested that periods 4, 5 and 6 had more elements than periods 1, 2 and 3 (periods 4, 5 and 6 have the blocks of transition elements).

The periodic table is a list of the elements in order of increasing atomic number. Those elements that have very similar properties (i.e. they form a group) are put one above the other (this works best for groups **1, 2, 7** and **0**).

The periods are arranged horizontally:
lithium, beryllium, boron, carbon, nitrogen, oxygen, fluorine and **neon** form one period.

The groups are arranged vertically: lithium, sodium, potassium, rubidium, caesium and francium form a group. The elements in a group have similar properties because the members of a group have the same arrangement of electrons in the outer shell (remember that most of chemistry involves the electrons in the outer shell). Three groups are looked at on the next page (the noble gases, the alkali metals and the halogens).

Have another look at pages 54, 55 and 56 (particuluarly 54 and 56) where this is first covered.

the connection between the arrangement of outer electrons and the position of an element in the periodic table;

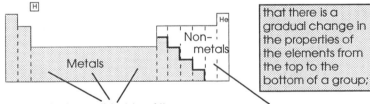

that there is a gradual change in the properties of the elements from the top to the bottom of a group;

As a general rule, on this side of the table, elements become more reactive as you move down a column i.e. Sodium is more reactive than Lithium.

On the non–metal side the reverse is true. In group VI and VII the most reactive element is found at the top of each column.

Property	Metals	Non-metals
Melting point	Usually high	Usually low
Appearance	Shiny when polished	Dull
Effect of bending and hammering	They can be bent or hammered into shapes	They are brittle and so snap or crumble
Electrical & thermal conductivity	Good conductors	Poor conductors (except graphite)

K. S. 4 Materials and their Properties	Patterns of behaviour	that elements in the same group of the periodic table have similar properties;

the periodic table

Some reactions of metals and non-metals

	metallic elements	non-metallic elements
with water	The more reactive metals react with water to give metal hydroxides and hydrogen.	Most non-metals do not react with water.
with oxygen	Many metals combine with oxygen to form metal oxides, e.g. calcium oxide (CaO). **If** these oxides dissolve in water, they give an **alkaline solution.**	Most non-metals combine with oxygen to form oxides, e.g. sulphur dioxide (SO_2). **If** these oxides dissolve in water, they give an **acid solution.**
with acids	Many metals react with acids to give hydrogen and a salt.	Most non-metals do not react with acids.
with chlorine	Many metals react with chlorine to give soluble ionic salts (e.g. sodium chloride).	Most non-metals react with chlorine to form molecular substances.

Periodic table and combining powers

(left margin element list, top to bottom: t.m. Cs Ba La Ce Pr Nd Pm Sm Eu Gd Td Dy Ho Er Tm Yb Lu Hf Ta W Re Os Ir Pt Au Hg Tl Pb Bi Po At Rn Fr Ra Ac Th Pa U Np Pu Am Cm Bk Cf Es Fm Md No Lr — with "transition metals" and "actinide series" labels)

1	2			3	4	3	2	1	0	Combining powers
1	2			3	4	5	6	7	8	Numbers of electrons in the outermost shell

Metals (various)   Non-metals

Atoms of elements in these columns lose electrons during reactions (they form positive ions, cations).

Atoms of elements in these columns gain electrons during reactions when they react with metals (they form negative ions, anions).

Atoms in this column do not readily accept or donate electrons.

Noble gases (Helium, neon, argon, krypton, and xenon) These are so unreactive that they were some of the last elements to be discovered, (if gases won't react, how can we know that they are there).

Helium and argon are used to surround welding or hot light filaments and so stop the metals being oxidised. Krypton and xenon are used in high intensity lamps, neon and other noble gases are used in advertising lamps. They are all present in our atmosphere but the main source of helium is from natural gas. All noble gases are purified by low temperature fractional distillation.

I can't do a table showing their reaction because they will not take part in most common reactions.

Alkali metals (Group 1)	1. These are very reactive metals (they need to be stored under oil). They are shiny when cut but very quickly tarnish in air and so need to be stored under oil

the properties and reactions of the alkali metals;

2. They are soft enough to be cut with a knife.
3. They are less dense than water, and react strongly with it to form metal hydroxides which make very alkaline solutions (pH 12 or more).

Element	Symbol of ion	Flame colour	Reaction with water	Reaction with chlorine	Salts (e.g. nitrates, sulphates, carbonates)
Li	Li^+	Crimson red	Reacts to give hydrogen and an alkali, LiOH (aq)	Reacts on heating to give white $LiCl_{(s)}$	White crystalline solids which are soluble in water
Na	Na^+	Bright yellow	Reacts vigorously to give hydrogen and an alkali, NaOH (aq)	Vigorous reaction on heating to give white $NaCl_{(s)}$	White crystalline solids which are soluble in water
K	K^+	Lilac	Reacts violently to give hydrogen and an alkali, KOH (aq)	Very vigorous reaction to give white $KCl_{(s)}$	White crystalline solids which are soluble in water

the properties, reactions and uses of simple compounds of the alkali metals;

Properties & reactions of, & uses for NaCl

Sodium chloride (NaCl)

Properties   White   Soluble in water   m.p. 808°C

Reactions: (well ... one of them anyway)

$$2NaCl_{(s)} + 2H_2SO_4 \, (l) \longrightarrow 2NaHSO_{4(s)} + 2HCl_{(aq)}$$
sodium chloride + conc sulphuric acid ⟶ sodium hydrogen sulphate + hydrochloric acid

Uses: It is a raw material in the manufacture of chlorine, used in the preservation of meat and fish (e.g. bacon , haddock), it is essential in the diet of animals.

Properties & reactions of, & uses for Na_2CO_3

Sodium carbonate (Na_2CO_3)

Properties   White   Soluble in water   m.p. 851°C

Reaction   Reacts with acids to give a salt, water and carbon dioxide

$$Na_2CO_{3(s)} + 2HCl_{(aq)} \longrightarrow 2NaCl \, (aq) + H_2O + CO_{2(g)}$$

Uses: Used in the manufacture of glass, paper, soap and detergents,

Properties & reactions of, & uses for $NaHCO_3$

Sodium hydrogen carbonate ($NaHCO_3$)

Properties   White   sparingly soluble in water   decomposes to Na_2CO_3

Reaction

$$NaHCO_{3(s)} + HCl \, (aq) \longrightarrow NaCl_{(s)} + 2H_2O_{(l)} + CO_2 \, (g)$$
sodium hydrogen carbonate + hydrochloric acid ⟶ sodium chloride + water + carbon dioxide

Uses: Baking powder, in firefighting equipment, pharmaceuticals.

K. S. 4 Materials and their Properties		
Patterns of behaviour	the periodic table	the properties, reactions and uses of simple compounds of the alkali metals (continued);

Properties & reactions of, & uses for NaOH

Sodium hydroxide (NaOH)

Properties Translucent white   very soluble in water   m.p. 318°C
solutions are very corrosive to the skin.

Reactions:

$$NaOH_{(s)} + HCl_{(aq)} \longrightarrow NaCl_{(s)} + 2H_2O_{(l)}$$

sodium hydroxide + hydrochloric acid $\longrightarrow$ sodium chloride + water

Uses: It is a very important substance in industry. It is used in in the manufacture of rayon, paper, aluminium, soap and detergents and in the petrochemical industry.

Halogens
Group 7

Halogens (Fluorine chlorine, bromine, iodine, and astatine) (astatine is very radioactive and has all decayed away, there is none to be found on Earth).

1. These are dangerous because they are very reactive non–metals.
2. Because they are so reactive they do not exist free in nature but are found as salts.
3. Most of them react with metals .
4. A great deal of energy is needed to purify them because they are so reactive.
5. They are usually purified by using electrolysis.

the properties, reactions and uses of simple compounds of the halogens;

Some of the elements in chemical **group 7** and their properties

Element	Symbol for the ion	Colour of vapour	Structure	Colour and state at room temperature	Potassium salt
Cl	Cl^-	Green	Molecules $Cl_2(g)$	Green gas	White crystalline solid, KCl (s) soluble in water
Br	Br^-	Orange–brown	Molecules $Br_2(g)$	Dark red-brown liquid	White crystalline solid, KBr (s) soluble in water
I	I^-	Purple	Molecules $I_2(g)$	Black solid with slight sheen	White crystalline solid, KI (s) soluble in water

The halogens have been used to make many useful substances which could be used as rust removers (e.g. by dipping the metal in HCl before painting) degreasing solvents, anaesthetics, pesticides, plastics (PVC) and a non-stick substance (PTFE).
Unfortunately many of the pesticides have later been shown to be quite harmful to the environment. DDT, dieldrin and aldrin are no longer used in most of the world because of these damaging effects.
In addition, the anaesthetics like chloroform need to be used sparingly because of the harm that they do to the liver and heart.

Transition metals

Let us start by looking again at some properties of elements in groups 1 & 2

The metals of groups 1 and 2 are reactive e.g. K, Na, Ca, Mg.

They have much lower densities, melting and boiling points compared to the transition metals.

1. Transition metals have high melting points and higher boiling points.
2. They have high densities.
3. They do not react readily with water.
4. Many have more than one combining power e.g. copper atoms can have a combining power of 1 or 2, iron atoms can have a combining power of 2 or 3.
5. Their compounds are coloured e.g:
   some copper compounds are blue
   some iron compounds are green,
   some nickel compounds are green.

1. Transition metals are used to make alloys and build bridges, ships, cars, trains, reinforced concrete i.e. iron.
2. Many are good conductors of electricity and are used for wiring e.g. copper.
3. They are used for non-corroding electrical contacts and jewellery e.g. gold, silver and platinum.
4. They can be used as catalysts e.g. platinum, nickel and iron.

rates of reactions

What must be happening during chemical reactions

Collision theory

Before they can react, molecules or ions have to bump into each other and the collision must be a hard one (hard enough to bring about bond breaking).

Only a small fraction of the collisions which take place are violent enough to bring about a reaction.

To speed up reactions, we must make the particles collide more vigorously and more often.

Examples of variations in the rates of reactions

Slow reactions:
1. The lime mortar holding bricks together contains $Ca(OH)_2$ and this reacts with CO_2 in the air to change to $CaCO_3$ and H_2O. This reaction takes place over the first 100 years after the bricks were laid.
2. Iron rusts slowly in moist air.

Medium rate reactions:
1. Sulphuric acid and lumps of zinc will produce a steady stream of hydrogen at room temperature.
2. Powdered carbon reacts with the oxygen in the air to produce a glowing mass when it is heated.

Fast reactions:
1. Mixing solutions of silver nitrate and sodium chloride produces insoluble silver chloride almost immediately.
2. The ingredients in gunpowder react violently (but not as quickly as the ingredients in cordite).

K. S. 4 Materials and their Properties	Patterns of behaviour

how the rates of reactions can be altered by varying temperature or concentration, or by changing the surface area of a solid reactant, or by adding a catalyst;

There are six ways to speed up the reaction

1. Make the reactants more concentrated.
2. Grind up the solids so that they have a bigger surface area.
3. Raise the temperature.
4. Shake the reactants more vigorously so that more mixing takes place.
5. Squash the gases by increasing the pressure on them (this has the same effect as making the reactants more concentrated).
6. Use a catalyst (for best results use a catalyst with large surface area).

Catalysts

We can also get reactions to happen at lower temperatures because some substances (we call them 'catalysts') have surfaces onto which the reacting chemicals can stick in the right position to react (not all catalysts work like this though e.g. H^+ ions). Chemists say that the catalysts have their effect because they reduce the activation energy, i.e. they allow the reactions to happen when the particles are moving more slowly.

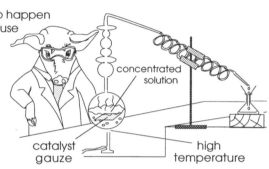

concentrated solution

catalyst gauze

high temperature

Catalyst (a definition with two examples)

A catalyst speeds up a reaction without itself being affected by the reaction e.g. a mixture of **silica and aluminium oxide** is used in the cracking of petroleum.
Many transition metals are used as catalysts (e.g. platinum used as **platinum/rhodium gauze**, is one catalyst in nitric acid manufacture).
Although catalysts are not affected by the reaction that they catalyse, they often operate at high temperatures and pressures and changes occur so that they need replacing after a while. **N.B.** Catalysts speed up the reaction in both directions (see the bottom of the next page).

reactions involving enzymes

Enzymes

Enzymes are biological catalysts (i.e. they speed up a reaction without being affected by the reaction).
They are made mainly of protein but often with metal ions as an important part of the molecule.
Being proteins they have the properties of many proteins:
1. They are damaged and change their shape if the temperature rises much above 40°C.
2. They are destroyed (inactivated) if the pH changes too far from their working pH.
In addition:
3. They are often very specific i.e. a particular enzyme may catalyse only one type of reaction, a particular reaction or even only a part of a reaction.
4. They are very effective catalysts. As an example, one of the faster acting enzymes is able to break down H_2O_2 to H_2O and O_2 at the rate of 40 000 molecules broken down per second.

$$2H_2O_2 \longrightarrow 2H_2O + O_2$$

(continued)

Enzymes and temperature

All chemical reactions are affected by temperature. Most reactions speed up as the temperature increases and enzymes are no exception to this general rule.

But . . . enzymes are proteins and so begin to change their shape when the temperature rises above 40°C (they get knocked out of shape by colliding particles in the medium around them as well as by vibrations of atoms within the protein molecule itself).

how rates of enzyme-catalysed reactions vary with temperature;

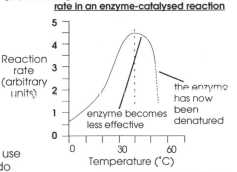

A graph showing how temperature affects reaction rate in an enzyme-catalysed reaction

Enzymes in the home and in industry

For a long time people have made use of enzyme systems in organisms to do certain tasks for them.

the use of enzymes in the baking, brewing and dairy industries;

1. Enzymes in yeast have been used to produce the bubbles that make bread nice to eat. Yeasts give off CO_2 as they use sugars during respiration.
2. Yeasts are also used to produce alcohol from grape juice or other sugary liquids. (yes . . . alcohol is produced as the bread rises but is evaporated off during the baking; you'd have to eat an awful lot of raw dough to get drunk, like enough to make you a seriously unwell person)
3. In the dairy industry bacteria and fungi are used to produce yoghurt and cheeses with different flavours.
4. Meat tenderiser.

They have also learned how to use separate enzymes and these are now becoming increasingly important.

4. Rennet, extracted from calf's stomach, curdles milk without affecting the flavour and so is used in the cheese industry as it allows much more control over the final flavour.
5. Starch digesting enzymes have been extracted from germinating grain. The enzymes are fixed to resin beads in a long bead-filled column. Boiled starch solution is then allowed to trickle down the column so that the starch is digested and glucose syrup comes out of the bottom. This means that sugar can be made from any cheap source of starch and people do not have to rely on sugar cane sugar or sugar beet sugar (which is quite bad news for 3rd World sugar producers).

that some reactions are reversible;

Reversible reactions

Two examples

Many reactions are reversible. This is particularly true of reactions that have been catalysed by enzymes.

When calcium carbonate is heated strongly (to 1000°C) it decomposes to calcium oxide and carbon dioxide. If this is done in a closed container so that the products build up, the reaction begins to go both ways i.e. the carbonate breaks down and is reformed. We use two arrows to show that this is happening thus: $\rightleftharpoons$

$$CaCO_3(s) \rightleftharpoons CaO(s) + CO_2(g)$$

and reacting hydrogen and iodine in a closed container

$$H_2(g) + I_2(g) \rightleftharpoons 2HI(g)$$

(continued)

| K. S. 4 Materials and their Properties | Patterns of behaviour | reversible reactions |

Chasing reactions backwards

By choosing the right conditions we can drive the reaction forwards or backwards. If we heat $CaCO_3$ in a closed container we get CaO and CO_2 as shown on the previous

> how the yield of products from reversible reactions depends on the conditions;

page. After a while an equilibrium is reached in which the products are formed as fast as they are recombining (this is referred to as a state of dynamic equilibrium).

1. If we increase the pressure in the container more gases will combine to give $CaCO_3$ i.e. the reaction will be pushed to the left.
2. If we remove the products as fast as they are produced the reaction will never reach equilibrium i.e. it will have shifted to the right.

This idea of shifting the reaction one way or the other is used both in industry and in nature.

> that some manufacturing processes are based on reversible reactions;

In industry the idea is to keep the reaction working with as great a yield as possible and often this is achieved by removing the products as they form.

In nature feedback by the products is very important in controlling the rates of reactions in cells. The reactions cannot just proceed each at their own rate as this would allow the buildup of some products, the shortage of others.

Many of the reactions are controlled by product feedback.

Consider the reaction sequence:

$$A \xrightarrow{\text{enzyme 1 speeds up A to B}} B \xrightarrow{\text{enzyme 2 speeds up B to C}} C$$

The reaction can be controlled if product C inhibits enzyme 1. As product C builds up, it will inhibit the production of B. There will therefore be less B and so the concentration of C will fall thus removing the inhibition on the first reaction.

| energy transfer in reactions | that changes of temperature often accompany reactions; | that reactions can be exothermic or endothermic; |

Exothermic reaction

During an exothermic reaction heat is given out and the chemicals may feel warm. They may even glow or there may be a flame.

Endothermic reaction

During an endothermic reaction there is a decrease in the temperature of the surroundings.

During chemical reactions, the bonds holding atoms or ions together break and then new bonds form, linking the atoms or ions together in different ways.

> that making and breaking chemical bonds in chemical reactions involves energy transfers.

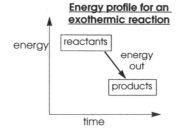

Energy profile for an exothermic reaction

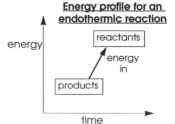

Energy profile for an endothermic reaction

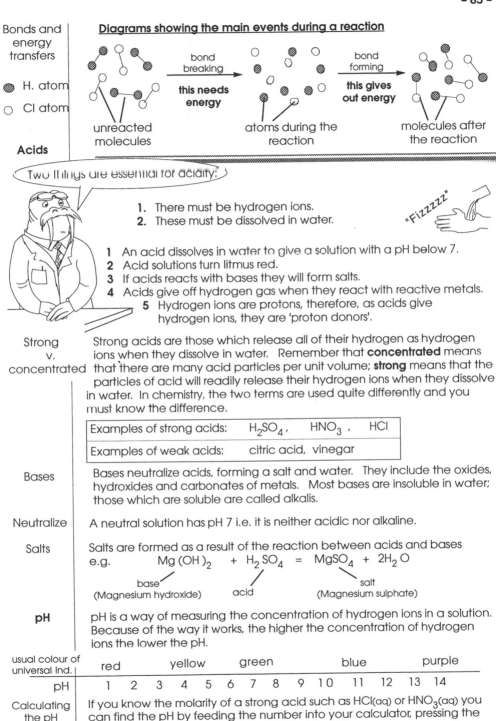

Bonds and energy transfers

Diagrams showing the main events during a reaction

⦿ H. atom
○ Cl atom

unreacted molecules → bond breaking **this needs energy** → atoms during the reaction → bond forming **this gives out energy** → molecules after the reaction

Acids

Two things are essential for acidity:

1. There must be hydrogen ions.
2. These must be dissolved in water.

"Fizzzzz"

1 An acid dissolves in water to give a solution with a pH below 7.
2 Acid solutions turn litmus red.
3 If acids reacts with bases they will form salts.
4 Acids give off hydrogen gas when they react with reactive metals.
5 Hydrogen ions are protons, therefore, as acids give hydrogen ions, they are 'proton donors'.

Strong v. concentrated

Strong acids are those which release all of their hydrogen as hydrogen ions when they dissolve in water. Remember that **concentrated** means that there are many acid particles per unit volume; **strong** means that the particles of acid will readily release their hydrogen ions when they dissolve in water. In chemistry, the two terms are used quite differently and you must know the difference.

Examples of strong acids:	H_2SO_4, HNO$_3$, HCl
Examples of weak acids:	citric acid, vinegar

Bases

Bases neutralize acids, forming a salt and water. They include the oxides, hydroxides and carbonates of metals. Most bases are insoluble in water; those which are soluble are called alkalis.

Neutralize

A neutral solution has pH 7 i.e. it is neither acidic nor alkaline.

Salts

Salts are formed as a result of the reaction between acids and bases
e.g. $Mg(OH)_2$ + H_2SO_4 = $MgSO_4$ + $2H_2O$

base (Magnesium hydroxide)   acid   salt (Magnesium sulphate)

pH

pH is a way of measuring the concentration of hydrogen ions in a solution. Because of the way it works, the higher the concentration of hydrogen ions the lower the pH.

usual colour of universal Ind.	red	yellow	green		blue	purple
pH	1 2 3	4 5	6 7 8	9 10	11 12	13 14

Calculating the pH

If you know the molarity of a strong acid such as HCl(aq) or HNO$_3$(aq) you can find the pH by feeding the number into your calculator, pressing the log button, and then changing the sign to positive.

K. S. 4 Physical Processes	Electricity and magnetism

Topic flow chart

definitions

energy

circuits

current effects

resistance

mains electricity

energy and potential difference in circuits

It is important to be familiar with the terms used in dealing with electricity.

This page is just an outline, the next 18 pages (and the questions in the Question Book) give us lots of practice.

Reading through is not the same as knowing !

Energy
Energy is something that can do work. If we lift an apple we have done work on it. (We have moved a force through a distance)

If we lift it one metre we have done a joule of work.

Work
Work = Force x distance

The apple will have gained a joule of energy.

Power
Power is a rate (because it is a rate there will be time in the units). It is the rate at which energy is transferred i.e. the rate at which work is done.

There is just too much info. per line

Summary table

Physical quantity	Name of the unit	Symbol
Energy	joule	J
Work	joule	J
Power	joules per second	Js^{-1} (i.e. a watt)

Charge Q
Charge is the property of electrons and protons that makes them attract each other (and repel their own kind). (it is not exactly a brilliant definition but that is one of the problems with physics, several of the quantities are quite hard to define. One such is charge; you can't see it, touch it or smell it but it does produce effects and so we define it in terms of these effects; hence: like charges repel, unlike charges attract. Charges can be + or –.). Charge is measured in coulombs (Q is a shorthand for charge).

One coulomb is the amount of charge that is carried by 6.24×10^{18} electrons.

Current I
Current is a rate of flow.
It is the rate at which negative charges pass in one direction or the rate at which positive charges pass in the opposite direction.
Current is measured in coulombs per second. (I is the symbol for current).

Potential difference V
Potential difference is the rate at which energy is being transferred.

that voltage is the energy transferred per unit charge;

It is measured in joules per coulomb (A volt is 1 joule per coulomb that passes) It has become acceptable to use Voltage for when we refer to potential difference. (This is a bit like using miles per hourage when really we mean speed but, in the case of PD, everyone seems to do it now)

Resistance R
The resistance of a conductor (e.g. a piece of silver wire) will influence the amount of current that will pass. The higher the resistance the smaller the current. The potential difference also affects the size of the current so we link the three in a single equation and use that to define resistance:

the quantitative relationship between resistance, voltage and current;

$$R = \frac{V}{I}$$

The info must be broken down into bits and this is best done by doing calculations

Electrical power	$P = IV$	the quantitative relationship between power, voltage and current
		but the units for I are coulombs per second and the units for PD are joules per coulomb

A circuit (with labels)

how to measure current in series and parallel circuits; how to make a simple measurement of voltage;

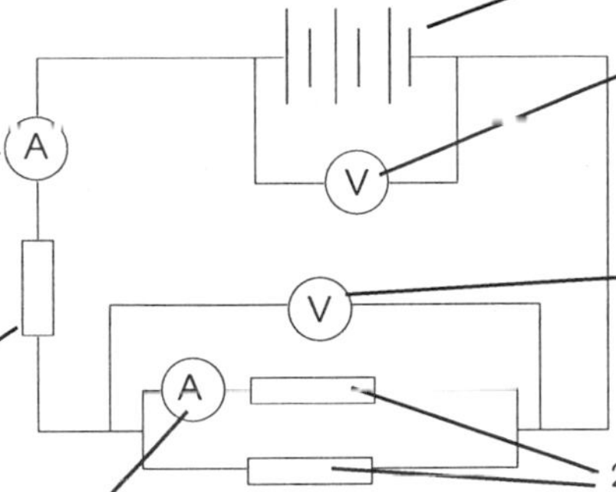

three cells making up a battery

voltmeter in parallel

voltmeters give an idea of the amount of energy being transferred

ammeter in series

ammeters measure current

(N.B.) the voltage across each of the resistors in parallel will be the same

resistor in series

2 resistors in parallel

an ammeter being used to measure the current flowing through one of the resistors

Currents and accountancy

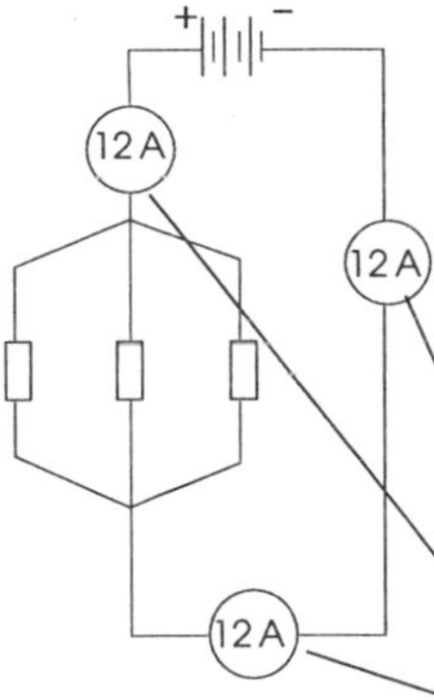

No electricity will flow in a particular part of a circuit if there are any breaks in the wires.

Electrons are good accountants, none of them get lost at any junctions.

In this circuit the current splits up at the junction in a very predictable way. One wire branches into three and so if we know any three currents, we can work out the fourth.

The current is the same at these three points (12 amps) because there are no junctions in that part of the circuit.

Part of the circuit (above left)

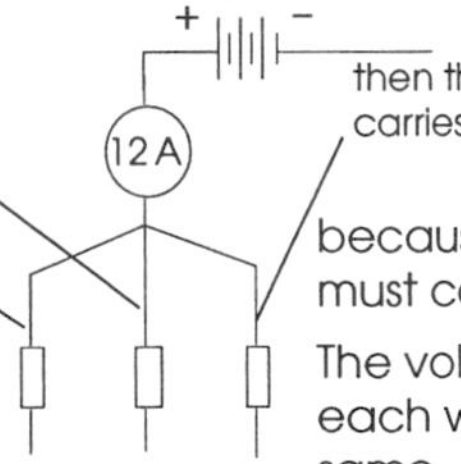

if this carries 4A
and this carries 3A
then this carries 5A
because the three must carry 12 amps.
The voltage across each will be the same.

that resistors are heated when charge flows through them;

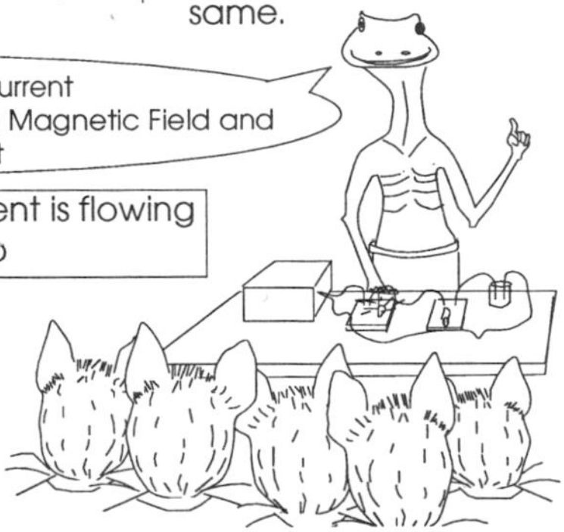

Three effects produced by an electric current

And here we have it, current can produce three effects! Heat, a Magnetic Field and a Chemical Effect

The medium through which the current is flowing (the wire, air or solution) will warm up

A magnetic field will be produced around the moving charge carriers

If the current flows through a solution of salts then the salts will be split i.e. electrolysed (see page 95)

Energy transfers

that energy is transferred from batteries and other sources to other components in electrical circuits;

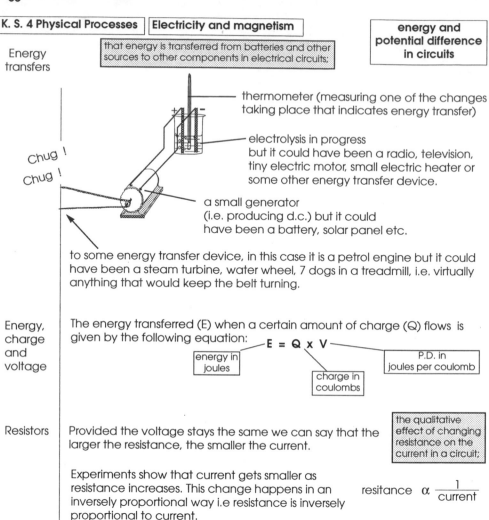

thermometer (measuring one of the changes taking place that indicates energy transfer)

electrolysis in progress but it could have been a radio, television, tiny electric motor, small electric heater or some other energy transfer device.

Chug !
Chug !

a small generator (i.e. producing d.c.) but it could have been a battery, solar panel etc.

to some energy transfer device, in this case it is a petrol engine but it could have been a steam turbine, water wheel, 7 dogs in a treadmill, i.e. virtually anything that would keep the belt turning.

Energy, charge and voltage

The energy transferred (E) when a certain amount of charge (Q) flows is given by the following equation:

$$E = Q \times V$$

energy in joules

charge in coulombs

P.D. in joules per coulomb

Resistors

Provided the voltage stays the same we can say that the larger the resistance, the smaller the current.

the qualitative effect of changing resistance on the current in a circuit;

Experiments show that current gets smaller as resistance increases. This change happens in an inversely proportional way i.e resistance is inversely proportional to current.

$$\text{resistance} \; \alpha \; \frac{1}{\text{current}}$$

how current varies with voltage in a range of devices, including resistors, filament bulbs, diodes, light dependant resistors (LDRs) and thermistors;

I-V graphs

Two sketch graphs showing how voltage affects current in different devices

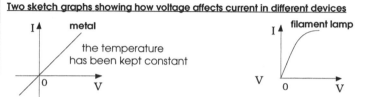

metal

the temperature has been kept constant

filament lamp

Metals and alloys give I-V graphs which are straight lines passing through the origin.
We call these **ohmic conductors**.

This graph (of a torch bulb) shows that the resistance increases at larger values of V. The temperature increases and for metals and alloys, the resistance usually rises as the temperature increases.

Two sketch graphs showing how voltage affects current in different devices

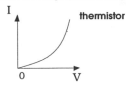

thermistor

semiconductor diode

These are made of semiconductors and for most of them, their resistance decreases sharply as the temperature rises.

LDR

In the dark the light dependant resistor has a very high resitance.

In bright light the resistance is low.

The graph shows that the current is almost zero when the p.d. is applied in one direction but it rises quite sharply when the p.d. acts in the opposite direction.

These are very useful for getting current to flow in one direction only, i.e. changing a.c. to d.c.

Measuring resistance (measured in ohms)

Glad, who feels the cold...quite badly at times (she's a six year old mother of 39), keeps an eye on the temperature, in between changing the resistor value and then measuring the voltage and current.

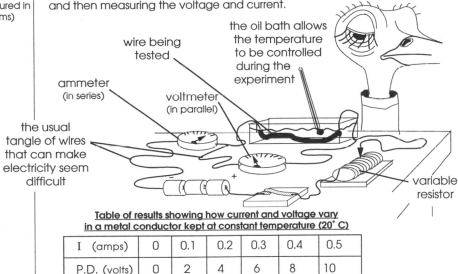

the oil bath allows the temperature to be controlled during the experiment

wire being tested

ammeter (in series)

voltmeter (in parallel)

the usual tangle of wires that can make electricity seem difficult

variable resistor

Table of results showing how current and voltage vary in a metal conductor kept at constant temperature (20° C)

I (amps)	0	0.1	0.2	0.3	0.4	0.5
P.D. (volts)	0	2	4	6	8	10

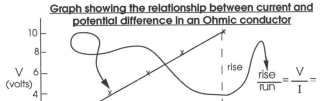

Graph showing the relationship between current and potential difference in an Ohmic conductor

V (volts)

I (amperes)

rise

run

If P.D. is in volts and the current is in amperes then the units for resistance will be ohms.

$$\frac{rise}{run} = \frac{V}{I} = \text{Resistance}$$

i.e. slope gives us resistance

$$R = \frac{V}{I} = \frac{8}{0.4} = 20\Omega$$

K. S. 4 Physical Processes	Electricity and magnetism

Ohm's law | The current flowing through a wire at constant temperature is proportional to the potential difference between its ends.

Limitations | This law is only obeyed when all the physical conditions remain constant, e.g. resistance can alter if the wire is bent or stretched or if it is placed at right angles to a magnetic field.
Many of the components used in radios (transistors etc.) do not obey Ohm's law.

---

d.c. | A direct current keeps flowing in the same direction. Usually this flow is fairly steady.

The voltage does not keep changing and so there is no need to find average voltages.

mains electricity

the difference between direct current and alternating current;

Conventional current | People have agreed (i.e. it is the convention) to pretend that current flows from positive to negative. Rules like the left hand rule etc. assume this.

Graph showing how a.c. voltage changes over 1.75 cycles

a.c. | Alternating current is an electric current that periodically reverses its direction in the circuit.
The voltage changes smoothly from negative to positive values and back again.

peak voltages

P.D. (V)
+3 2 1 0 1 2 −3

Time

RMS value

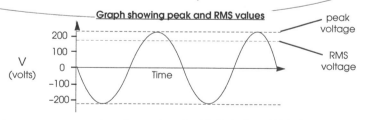

In the graph above the voltage changes from a positive value to an equivalent negative value over and over again. The simple average for this will be zero.

There is a way around this:
1. Square all the voltage values through a cycle (this will change the negative values to positive values)
2. Add all the values and find the mean. 3. Take the square root of the mean. We now the root mean square value.

Graph showing peak and RMS values

peak voltage

RMS voltage

V (volts)
200 100 0 −100 −200

Time

Topic flow

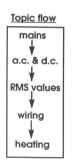

mains
↓
a.c. & d.c.
↓
RMS values
↓
wiring
↓
heating

The root mean square values for mains electricity in the U.K. is 240V.
The peak voltage is 1.4142 times larger i.e. 240 x 1.4142 =339.4 V
The RMS voltage is 0.707 times the value of the peak voltage

$$\sqrt{2} \times \text{peak voltage} = \text{RMS} \quad (\sqrt{2} \approx 1.4142)$$

Frequency | The voltage in the mains keeps changing 100 times a second
i.e. there are 50 complete cycles every second. (i.e. 50 hertz . . . 50 Hz)

Electricity: Increasing use and the need for safety	1. Homes, that once ran on human power, wood and coal for heating, now run with electricity guided by humans and oil or gas (or coal) for heating. 2. Our electricity is supplied to the home at 220–240V (110V in America) and can kill. 3. We therefore have built in safety measures to make sure that deaths are kept to a minimum.	the functions of the live, neutral and earth wires in the domestic mains supply, the use of insulation, earthing, fuses and circuit breakers to protect users of electrical equipment.

The three point plug

The electricity supply cable to your house contains two wires.

A **live** wire and a **neutral** wire.

The neutral wire is earthed at the power station and so the voltage between it and the ground is zero. The voltage between the live wire and the ground is 220–240V. The live wire is therefore very dangerous.

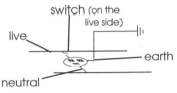

A diagram showing the connections to a three point plug

Power station to plug

A diagram showing the main features of the power supply to a set of plugs in the home: Power Station . . . Consumer Service unit . . . Ring Main . . . Plugs

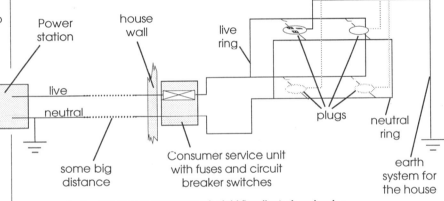

The earth at work

A diagram showing how current might flow through an heater

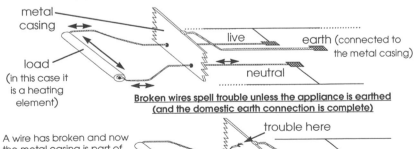

Broken wires spell trouble unless the appliance is earthed (and the domestic earth connection is complete)

A wire has broken and now the metal casing is part of the circuit. Luckily, this is earthed. As the resistance is now much lower (in this case) the current is high enough to melt the fuse i.e. it 'blows'.

Fires are prevented because the current stops before any wires have a chance to get very hot.

K. S. 4 Physical Processes	Electricity and magnetism	energy and potential difference in circuits

Circuit breakers

Circuit breakers are found in the consumer supply box. They automatically switch off when a large current surge occurs. This means that, should a fault occur in the system, the current is cut off almost immediately. Switching them back on again is much easier than replacing the older style wire fuses (particularly in the dark)

Single circuit breakers are also found on electric kettles and other appliances. They can cut off the supply when the device overheats.

Earth leakage

Earth leakage switches off the mains if any current flows along the earth wire. As electricity only flows along the earth wire when there is a fault, this is a further safety device. Some earth leakage systems are sensitive enough to be triggered when lightning strikes the power lines nearby. This can be a real problem if you have just packed your freezer to the top and then left for two weeks holiday.

Double insulation

If an appliance is double insulated it does not need the earth wire. A two pin plug may be used. Such appliances are designed so that the wires supplying the current can never come into contact with a metal casing. Plastics have made this possible.

Now is the time to copy out the diagrams on the last page without looking.

and then check for mistakes. Use a different colour to show the path followed by the current as it surges back and forth in all three diagrams.

Electricity has made a huge difference to the quality of life in the home.

the electrical heating is used in a variety of ways in domestic contexts;

Least expensive

1. It has allowed us to extend the day by lighting our homes during the evening.
2. It has made possible high quality entertainment in our homes with radios, music systems and television.

Still not expensive

3. It has taken the drudgery out of the cleaning carpets and floors, dusting cupboard tops (vacuum cleaners) and has made preparation of food much quicker and less tiring (blenders, mixers and processors).
4. Washing clothes was an exhausting business (particularly the washing of blankets, sheets, duvets etc) before the washing machine.

Most expensive in fact, quite costly

5. It can also be used for heating water (electric kettles and immersion heater).
6. Heating food (microwaves and electric cookers),
7. Heating the house (fan heaters, electric fires, and storage heaters).

Kilowatt hour (i.e. a unit)

The electricity boards charge customers by the kilowatt hour i.e. one joule per second transferred for an hour (one watt for an hour). The kilowatt hour is also known as a unit (7.15p per unit Sept. 1997).

how measurements of energy transferred are used to calculate the costs of using common domestic appliances;

electric charge	**points to note**

Static

1. Certain materials do not conduct electricity . e.g.. plastics, ceramics, amber.

Topic flow

statics (the basics)

↓

uses and dangers

↓

Q = It

2. If these are rubbed with wool, silk or fur, they become charged with either positive or negative charge. What has happened is that electrons have been rubbed off one (it has lost electrons so now it is positively charged) and onto the other (which becomes negatively charged). **The negative charges are due to electrons and the positive charges are due to protons in the nucleus. N.B. Only the electrons move.**

4. It seems that there are only two types of charge; scientists have agreed to call them "positive" and "negative".

Experiments have shown that:
  a like charges repel
  b unlike charges attract
  c. as with magnets, if two objects attract each other, only one of them may carry charge (or be a magnet). Repulsion is the true test.

charged polythene strip

uncharged conductor (on a nylon thread)

A bit philosophical this, but remember that "positive" and "negative" are just words that we use when referring to charge; the two charges are not positive or negative any more than the yellow fruit is "banana" or the grey friendly furry creature is "mouse" . **The word is not the object !**

Industrial examples of charge being made to work for us

Xerox copiers

An image of the document falls onto a charged metal drum, and parts of the drum are discharged.
Charged granules of graphite and resin stick to the parts of the drum that still carry charge and are transferred to paper. Heating the paper then fuses the resin to its fibres.

Sticking paint to metal

These are just insulating stands, not part of a revolutionary chicken-legged car.

metal part of the car that has been given positive charge

paint drops that carry negative charge so that they stick firmly to the metal

Removing dust from smoke

1. Give the particles a charge as they flow from the furnace as part of the smoke. At the same time give opposite charge to the metal plates in the precipitator.
2. Make the smoke flow past metal plates in the precipitator. The dust sticks to the plates.
3. Shake the plates so that the dust drops and can be removed (30 tonnes per hour for a medium power station).
4. This process removes 99% of the particulates.

chimney (99% of the dust has been removed)

flue-ash precipitator units with their charged metal plates

Static and safety

Whenever non-conductors are rubbed in a dry atmosphere, there will be a build up of static electricity. Static electricity can therefore build up on the plastic of petrol containers, the nozzles of grain shoots in silos, or the rollers in a paper mill. These must therefore be made of conducting material so that charge does not build up and cause sparks.

Pieces of oil tanker or paper mill, flour mill, half empty fuel tank, or any thing where static sparks can occur in a space filled with air or dust or fumes. The reason that explosions occur is because each little bit of burnable dust is surrounded by air and so when a fire starts, it will spread very quickly, i.e. there is an explosion!

"B O O M !"

about electric current as the flow of free electrons in metals or of ions during electrolysis,

Conductors and Non-Conductors

It is generally true that materials that conduct heat will also conduct electricity well. e.g. metals (see page 130)

Materials which are heat insulators (plastics, glass etc.) are also good electrical insulators.

Current

1. Metals conduct electricity because some of the electrons are free to move.
2. When there is no voltage across the metal, these 'free' electrons move about the crystal randomly (at speeds of about 0.001 x the speed of light).
3. When there is a voltage across the conductor they flow from the negative side to the positive side.
4. The net movement is quite slow: In a thin piece of copper wire carrying 1 amp, the electrons will take about 30 minutes to drift half a metre.
5. The electric field that causes the current to flow, spreads across the conductor at speeds very close to the the speed of light. This means that the current flows the moment you switch on the light (but the electrons do not travel very quickly).

Charge
carriers
(continued
from the last
page)

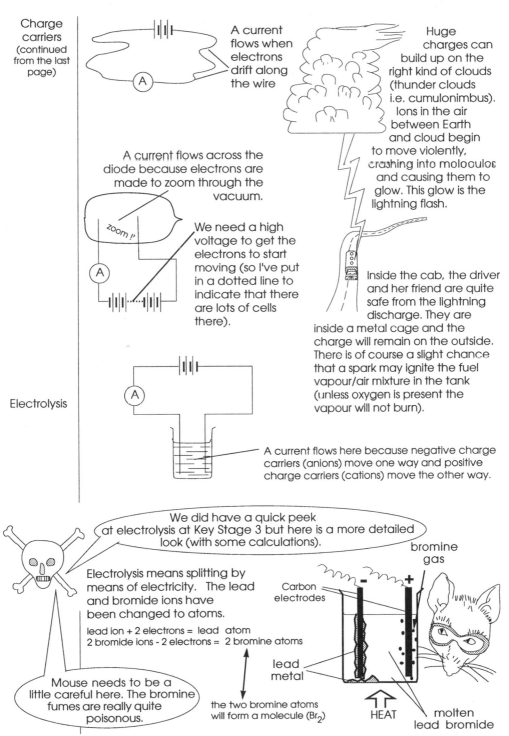

A current
flows when
electrons
drift along
the wire

A current flows across the
diode because electrons are
made to zoom through the
vacuum.

zoom !'

We need a high
voltage to get the
electrons to start
moving (so I've put
in a dotted line to
indicate that there
are lots of cells
there).

Huge
charges can
build up on the
right kind of clouds
(thunder clouds
i.e. cumulonimbus).
Ions in the air
between Earth
and cloud begin
to move violently,
crashing into molecules
and causing them to
glow. This glow is the
lightning flash.

Inside the cab, the driver
and her friend are quite
safe from the lightning
discharge. They are
inside a metal cage and the
charge will remain on the outside.
There is of course a slight chance
that a spark may ignite the fuel
vapour/air mixture in the tank
(unless oxygen is present the
vapour will not burn).

Electrolysis

A current flows here because negative charge
carriers (anions) move one way and positive
charge carriers (cations) move the other way.

We did have a quick peek
at electrolysis at Key Stage 3 but here is a more detailed
look (with some calculations).

bromine
gas

Electrolysis means splitting by
means of electricity. The lead
and bromide ions have
been changed to atoms.

Carbon
electrodes

lead ion + 2 electrons = lead atom
2 bromide ions - 2 electrons = 2 bromine atoms

lead
metal

Mouse needs to be a
little careful here. The bromine
fumes are really quite
poisonous.

the two bromine atoms
will form a molecule (Br_2)

HEAT

molten
lead bromide

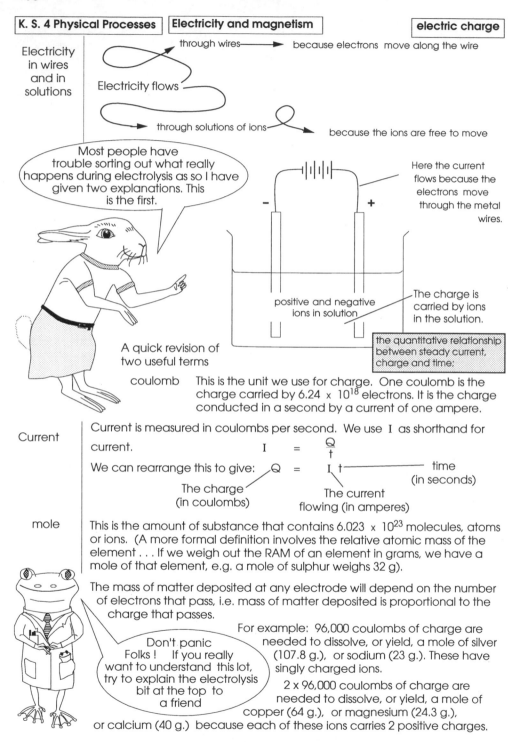

Electricity in wires and in solutions

Electricity flows

through wires ——▶ because electrons move along the wire

through solutions of ions — because the ions are free to move

Most people have trouble sorting out what really happens during electrolysis as so I have given two explanations. This is the first.

Here the current flows because the electrons move through the metal wires.

– +

positive and negative ions in solution

The charge is carried by ions in the solution.

A quick revision of two useful terms

the quantitative relationship between steady current, charge and time;

coulomb This is the unit we use for charge. One coulomb is the charge carried by 6.24×10^{18} electrons. It is the charge conducted in a second by a current of one ampere.

Current Current is measured in coulombs per second. We use I as shorthand for current.

$$I = \frac{Q}{t}$$

We can rearrange this to give: $Q = I\,t$ ———— time (in seconds)

The charge (in coulombs)

The current flowing (in amperes)

mole This is the amount of substance that contains 6.023×10^{23} molecules, atoms or ions. (A more formal definition involves the relative atomic mass of the element . . . If we weigh out the RAM of an element in grams, we have a mole of that element, e.g. a mole of sulphur weighs 32 g).

The mass of matter deposited at any electrode will depend on the number of electrons that pass, i.e. mass of matter deposited is proportional to the charge that passes.

For example: 96,000 coulombs of charge are needed to dissolve, or yield, a mole of silver (107.8 g.), or sodium (23 g.). These have singly charged ions.

Don't panic Folks ! If you really want to understand this lot, try to explain the electrolysis bit at the top to a friend

2 x 96,000 coulombs of charge are needed to dissolve, or yield, a mole of copper (64 g.), or magnesium (24.3 g.), or calcium (40 g.) because each of these ions carries 2 positive charges.

Calculation on electrolysis

We need to deposit 50 g of silver on a large trophy. Here is what we do!

1. Calculate how many moles this is.
2. Calculate how many coulombs of electricity must pass to achieve this.
3. Work out what current must flow and for how long.

relative atomic mass of silver = 107.87

number of moles in 50 g $= \dfrac{50}{107.87}$

$= 0.4635$ moles

Each mole needs 96,000 coulombs to be deposited

so we need $96{,}000 \times 0.4635$

$= 44\,496.2$ C

We know that $I = \dfrac{Q}{t}$ Let us plan to take 180 min. for the task (i.e. 10800 s)

$I = \dfrac{44\,496.2}{10800}$

$= 12.36$ amps.

You don't really need 4 decimal places in your answer but it is important not to round up during the calculation. Leave any rounding up until the end and **show all your calculations!**

Electrolysis a final look

electro lysis

This applies when we use **electricity** to **split** substances

chlorine gas

The metal ions will move to the negative electrode (cathode) and the chloride ions will move to the positive electrode (anode). Electrolysis occurs because the ions are free to move, i.e. when the salt is molten or in solution.

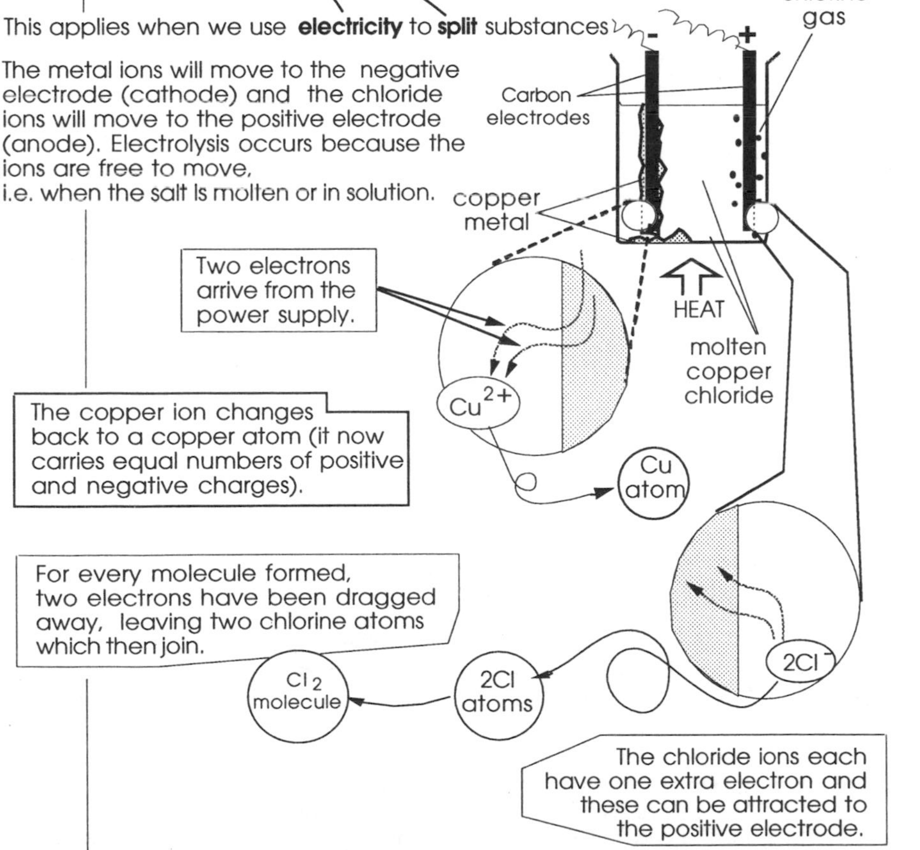

Carbon electrodes

copper metal

Two electrons arrive from the power supply.

HEAT

molten copper chloride

Cu^{2+}

The copper ion changes back to a copper atom (it now carries equal numbers of positive and negative charges).

Cu atom

For every molecule formed, two electrons have been dragged away, leaving two chlorine atoms which then join.

$2Cl^-$

Cl_2 molecule

2Cl atoms

The chloride ions each have one extra electron and these can be attracted to the positive electrode.

Field

We use the term field for a region in space that is under the influence of some physical agency e.g. a magnetic field is that region of space where a magnet is producing its effect.

that like magnetic poles repel and unlike magnetic poles attract.

The field lines around a bar magnet as shown with iron filings

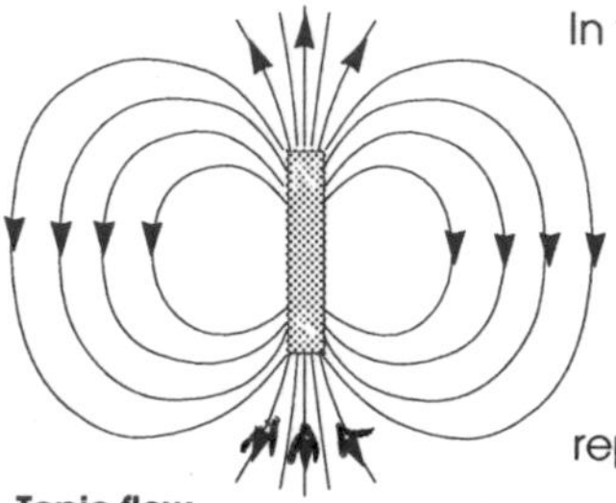

In the case of bar magnets it is quite easy to get some idea of the shape of this field by placing the magnet under a card and sprinkling iron filings on the card.

A few gentle taps and the filings arrange themselves into a pattern much like the one shown on the left.

Given two bar magnets to play with, we can show how their fields interact when we hold them so that they are repelling or attracting each other.

Topic flow

Magnets
↓
and fields
↓
motors

The field lines around bar magnets when like poles are together

The field lines around bar magnets when unlike poles are together

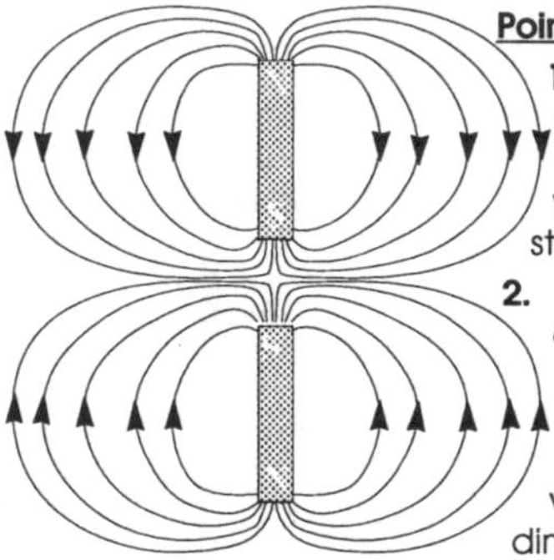

Points to note

1. The lines are closest together in those regions where the field is strongest.

2. These patterns only show a slice through the field, they do not show the whole three dimensional field.

Electric and gravitational fields

Electric charge and objects with mass produce fields (electric and gravitational fields). The pattern of the electric field can be seen by mixing grass seeds in oil, pouring this into a small tank and placing this between charged plates or probes.

Magnets

1. Any magnetized material placed in a magnetic field will swing itself round to fit in with the direction of the field lines (if it is free to move). The end which points to the Earth's north pole is the 'north seeking pole' ('north pole' for short).

2. Two north poles will repel, two south poles will repel. one north and one south will attract, i.e. opposite poles attract, like poles repel.

3. Only iron, cobalt and nickel are attracted to magnets. Substances such as aluminium, copper, brass, wood and glass are not attracted (All non-magnetic materials are affected if the magnet brought close to them is powerful enough).

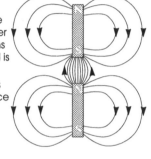

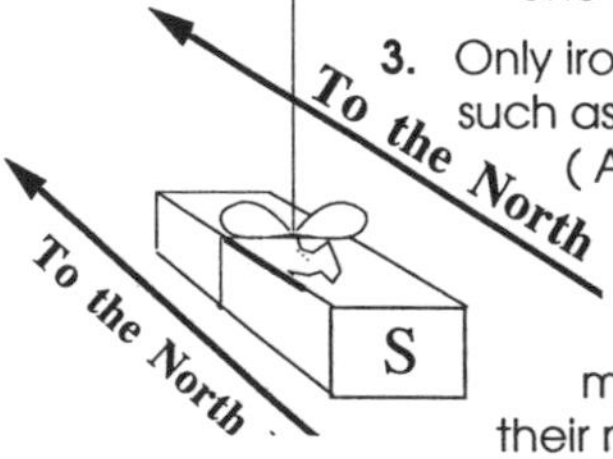

The alloys which are hardest to magnetise (e.g. Alnico) keep their magnetism for the longest time. Those which can be magnetised very easily (e.g. Soft iron and Mumetal) also lose their magnetism very easily, 'easy come, easy go!'

The Earth acts as a magnet with field lines reaching far out into space. We live and move deep inside this field. Many creatures are able to detect this field and can use it to find their way about. Every few thousand years, the Earth's magnetic North and South pole change ends. The Earth's magnetic poles keep shifting position a little every year.

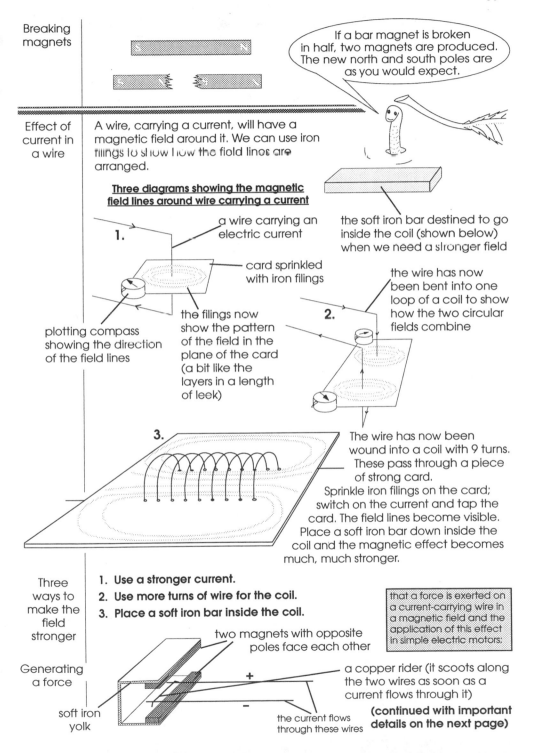

Breaking magnets

If a bar magnet is broken in half, two magnets are produced. The new north and south poles are as you would expect.

Effect of current in a wire

A wire, carrying a current, will have a magnetic field around it. We can use iron filings to show how the field lines are arranged.

the soft iron bar destined to go inside the coil (shown below) when we need a stronger field

Three diagrams showing the magnetic field lines around wire carrying a current

1.
a wire carrying an electric current

card sprinkled with iron filings

the filings now show the pattern of the field in the plane of the card (a bit like the layers in a length of leek)

plotting compass showing the direction of the field lines

2.
the wire has now been bent into one loop of a coil to show how the two circular fields combine

3.
The wire has now been wound into a coil with 9 turns. These pass through a piece of strong card.
Sprinkle iron filings on the card; switch on the current and tap the card. The field lines become visible. Place a soft iron bar down inside the coil and the magnetic effect becomes much, much stronger.

Three ways to make the field stronger

1. **Use a stronger current.**
2. **Use more turns of wire for the coil.**
3. **Place a soft iron bar inside the coil.**

that a force is exerted on a current-carrying wire in a magnetic field and the application of this effect in simple electric motors.

Generating a force

two magnets with opposite poles face each other

a copper rider (it scoots along the two wires as soon as a current flows through it)

soft iron yolk

the current flows through these wires

(continued with important details on the next page)

The important details	**Points to note** To predict the direction in which the wire will move we need to know the following: 1. the directions of the current (judged to be from positive to negative), 2. the direction of the magnetic field (judged to be towards the north pole). The wire movement is at right angles to both the magnetic field and to the current direction as set out by the left hand rule.
The left hand rule	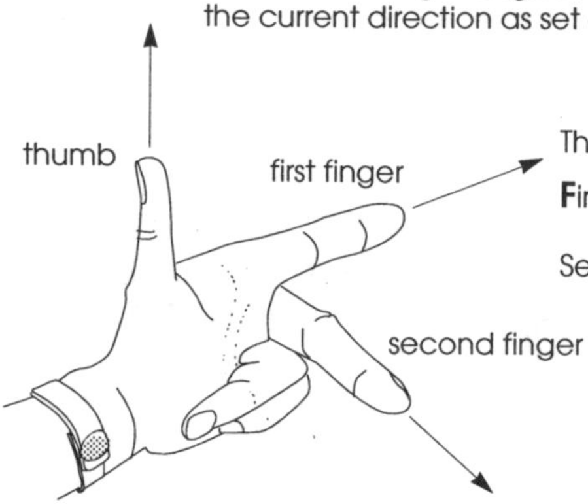 thumb first finger second finger Thumb → **m**otion First ——→ magnetic **f**ield (pointing towards the north pole) Se**c**ond → **C**urrent (finger pointing to the negative pole)

A diagram of a slice through a catapult field showing how the field lines are distorted

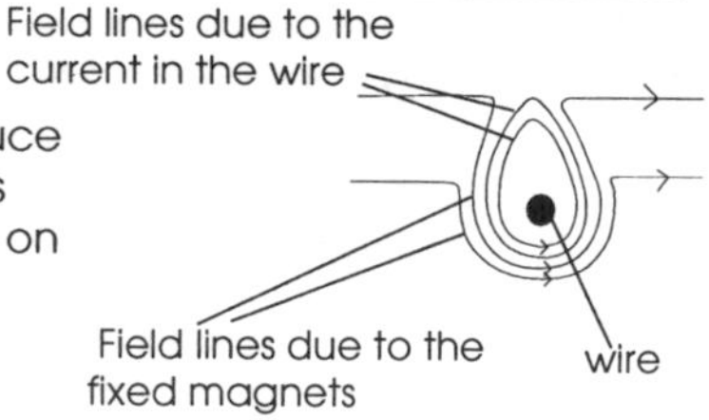

Field lines due to the current in the wire

Field lines due to the fixed magnets   wire

Catapult field	Two magnetic fields can interact to produce a force. The example shown on the right is called a catapult field because the force on the wire will tend to catapult it upwards.

Motor effect	**A slice through the field to show how a few of the field lines can interact**

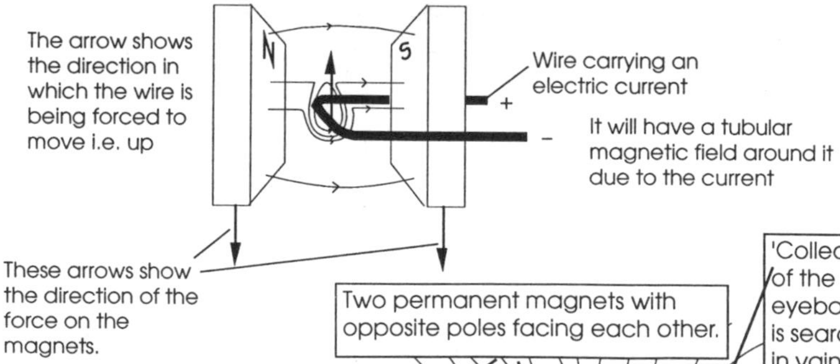

The arrow shows the direction in which the wire is being forced to move i.e. up

Wire carrying an electric current

It will have a tubular magnetic field around it due to the current

These arrows show the direction of the force on the magnets.

Two permanent magnets with opposite poles facing each other.

'Colleague' of the eyeball that is searching in vain for the catapult field. It's there, but not directly visible.

Work out which way the rotor will spin when a current flows.
The answer is at the top of the next page)

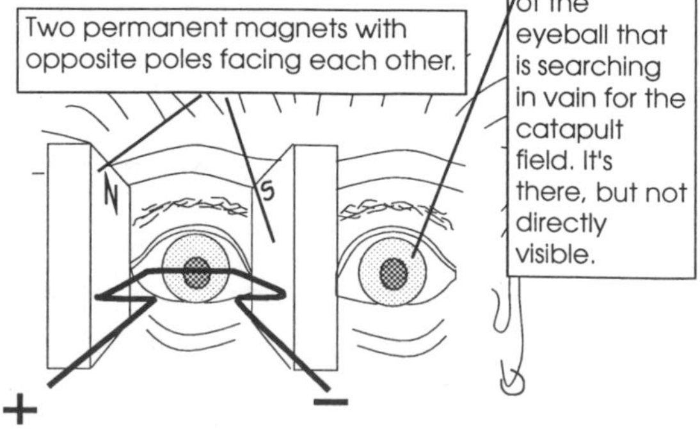

Making a
simple
motor

1. Take two magnets and
   set them so that opposite
   poles face each other

Answer (from page 100):
Left side down, right side up
i.e. anticlockwise as we look at it.

3. Use two little wires to lead electricity on
   and off the spinning wire. Set the whole lot
   on a board.

2. Bend a piece of wire and fit
   it between the two magnets
   so that it is free to spin

4. Now start adding more loops of wire. Add them in
   such a way that some of them will always be
   moving through the magnetic field (from the two
   permanent magnets) at right angles to the field
   lines.

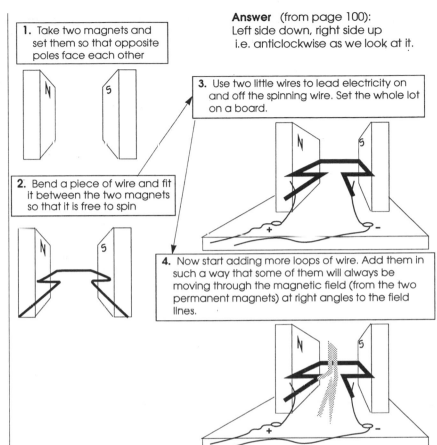

Electromagnetic induction

The bit from the National Curriculum on the right says much the
same thing in two different ways.

1. When a wire is moved in a magnetic field (as when we spin
   a generator or use a wire skipping rope in the Earth's
   magnetic field,) we will get a current.
2. When we produce a changing magnetic field (as happens
   inside a transformer or in the coils of some loudspeakers) a
   voltage is produced in any wires nearby.

*that a voltage is induced
when a conductor cuts
magnetic field lines and
when the magnetic field
though a coil changes;*

<u>Topic flow chart</u>
Inducing a voltage
↓
generators and a.c.
↓
transformers
↓
electricity supply

Electro-
magnetic
induction

Electro–magnetic induction

electricity   magnetism   using one to
                                produce the other

We can get a current to flow in a wire, by moving a magnet near the wire.
It doesn't really matter whether the magnet moves or the wire moves,
either way a current will flow.

Generators and alternators

Generators convert mechanical energy into electrical energy.

how simple a.c. generators and transformers work;

They can produce a current which flows steadily in only one direction or a current that keeps changing direction.

Dynamos produce direct current.

Alternators produce alternating current.

A motor acting as a generator

The motor diagram from the last page can also be used to show how a generator works. In each case we have a wire coil spinning in a magnetic field.

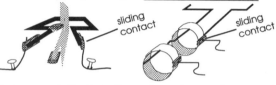

these are just two of many coils that are free to spin in the magnetic field.

the current will always be strongest in wires in the position of the black wire. In this position the conductor is cutting straight across the magnetic field lines (at right angles)

sliding contacts

Contacts for a d.c. generator   **Contacts for an alternator**

sliding contact   sliding contact

wires which make contact with the wires of the coil and allow the current generator to leave and flow in the outside circuit. These wires are called brushes.

Summary

1. Spin the coils and we get a current flowing in the wires.
2. Electrons can flow from the coil through the sliding contact on the left. They can flow back onto the coil through the contact on the right. In this way we have a d.c. current flowing through the outside circuit.
3. The current is d.c. because the wires on one side are always rising though the magnetic field, the wires on the other side are always passing down through the field.
4. In any one piece of wire in the coil the current is constantly changing direction.
5. If we arrange the brushes differently we will get a.c. flowing in the outside circuit.

Why electric motors should spin at the design speed

When we supply electrical energy to a motor, it spins and will do work.

When we spin the motor, it produces electricity i.e. it acts as a generator.

The device can be either motor or generator.

When we make it work as a motor it spins and, by spinning will produce a voltage that opposes the voltage driving the motor. Motors are designed to take this into account and so we should let them work at close to their top speed. If we don't, the **back – E.M.F.** due to the generator effect will be too small, the current through the motor will increase and the motor will overheat i.e. don't press so hard on the electric sander or drill that you slow down the motor noticeably.

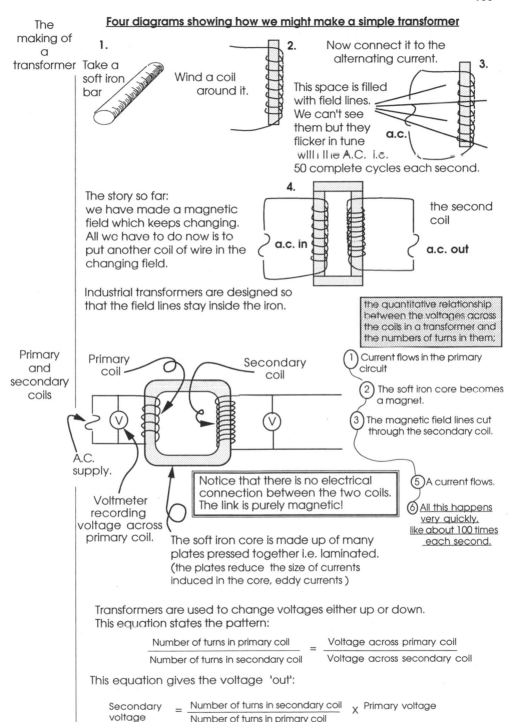

The making of a transformer

Four diagrams showing how we might make a simple transformer

1. Take a soft iron bar

Wind a coil around it.

2. Now connect it to the alternating current.

This space is filled with field lines. We can't see them but they flicker in tune with the A.C. i.e. 50 complete cycles each second.

3.

a.c.

The story so far: we have made a magnetic field which keeps changing. All we have to do now is to put another coil of wire in the changing field.

4.

a.c. in

the second coil

a.c. out

Industrial transformers are designed so that the field lines stay inside the iron.

the quantitative relationship between the voltages across the coils in a transformer and the numbers of turns in them.

Primary and secondary coils

Primary coil

Secondary coil

A.C. supply.

Voltmeter recording voltage across primary coil.

(1) Current flows in the primary circuit

(2) The soft iron core becomes a magnet.

(3) The magnetic field lines cut through the secondary coil.

Notice that there is no electrical connection between the two coils. The link is purely magnetic!

(5) A current flows.

(6) All this happens very quickly, like about 100 times each second.

The soft iron core is made up of many plates pressed together i.e. laminated. (the plates reduce the size of currents induced in the core, eddy currents)

Transformers are used to change voltages either up or down. This equation states the pattern:

$$\frac{\text{Number of turns in primary coil}}{\text{Number of turns in secondary coil}} = \frac{\text{Voltage across primary coil}}{\text{Voltage across secondary coil}}$$

This equation gives the voltage 'out':

$$\text{Secondary voltage} = \frac{\text{Number of turns in secondary coil}}{\text{Number of turns in primary coil}} \times \text{Primary voltage}$$

K. S. 4 Physical Processes	Electricity and magnetism	electromagnetic induction

| The electricity supply | Electricity is a very convenient way of transferring energy. We need only to obey certain rules about safety and we can relax and enjoy energy at the flick of a switch. | how electricity is generated and transmitted. |

Heat energy leaving the system as wasted energy.

Fumes (mainly carbon dioxide and sulphur dioxide) unless a scrubbing unit is fitted.

New designs for power stations try to use the heat that, in the past, had been wasted e.g. it can be used for factory heating. **Combined Heat and Power station.** Such a power station can have an efficiency of 70% or 80%, i.e. twice that for an electricity-only station.

cooling towers allow hot water to be cooled and used again (or be returned to the river without causing too much thermal pollution).

fuel into the power station.

High tension wires.

Features that all new power stations should have

Scrubbers on the smoke stack	**Electrostatic cleaner.**This uses static to attract and hold dust particles (usually 30 – 60 μm), see p.94. **Cyclone dust scrubber**. This uses the centrifuge principle to separate out larger particles (greater than 85 μm). **Chemical scrubbers** usually work because the fumes are forced though a fine liquid spray containing substances which will react with the sulphur dioxide.	μm: a millionth of a metre
Efficient burners	**Fluidized bed combustion** makes much more effective extraction of heat energy from the solid fuel (the process is still being developed).	
Reduction of all waste	**Waste heat used** to heat industrial complexes, greenhouses or houses, if the station is near a town.	

| Efficient energy transfers | The only time that there is complete transfer of energy is when it is transferred to heat. In all other transfers, a part of the energy will appear as heat. |

Example If you burn wood, all the energy will be transferred as heat. If you use the same wood to run a steam engine, only about 10% of the energy will appear as movement. The rest is given off as heat and sound. The figure for the petrol engine is about 30 %.

| Efficient energy transfers in the national grid | In the case of electricity it is the electrons that have to crash their way along the wires, continuously bumping into metal atoms and heating them up. This heating effect depends on the size of the current and so we try to keep the current as small as possible. Huge amounts of energy must still be transferred and so power lines operate at very high voltages i.e few coulombs but very many joules for each coulomb. |

Moving energy with the least waste

1. Electricity flows because electrons drift along the conductor.
2. As they drift they collide with particles in the conductor and so the conductor warms up.
3. The larger the current, the greater the heating effect and so more energy will be wasted (or transferred).
4. If we need to transfer a set amount of energy, this can best be done by using a small current and a very high voltage.

$$P = I \times V$$

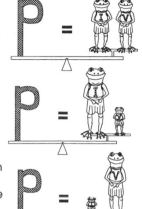

If you can figure out why these three see-saws are here you are half way to understanding why we use ac in the mains

In each of the three cases the same power is involved.

5. But we can't use high voltages in the home as they are dangerous.
6. Fortunately transformers will change voltages very efficiently (i.e. with very little energy loss).
7. But transformers will only work with a.c. and so we use a.c. in the national grid.

The National Grid

The voltages used

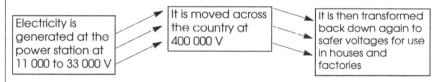

| Electricity is generated at the power station at 11 000 to 33 000 V | → | It is moved across the country at 400 000 V | → | It is then transformed back down again to safer voltages for use in houses and factories |

Compromises

To reduce the heat lost from the high tension power lines we ensure that they only carry a small current (just a few coulombs per second but each coulomb capable of transferring a great deal of energy i.e. the voltage is high).

If we use very high voltages there will be problems insulating the wires from the ground below and from the air around them. The pylons will be too big and expensive.

Transferring the energy at 400 000 joules per coulomb gives the best compromise.

Gosh! Sometimes it's just so hard to stay awake

The power lines are very much like the chain drive that connects a small petrol engine to a water pump. We try to design the chain so that as little as possible of the energy is transferred as heat i.e. even after the system has been running briskly for a few minutes the chain should not be hot.

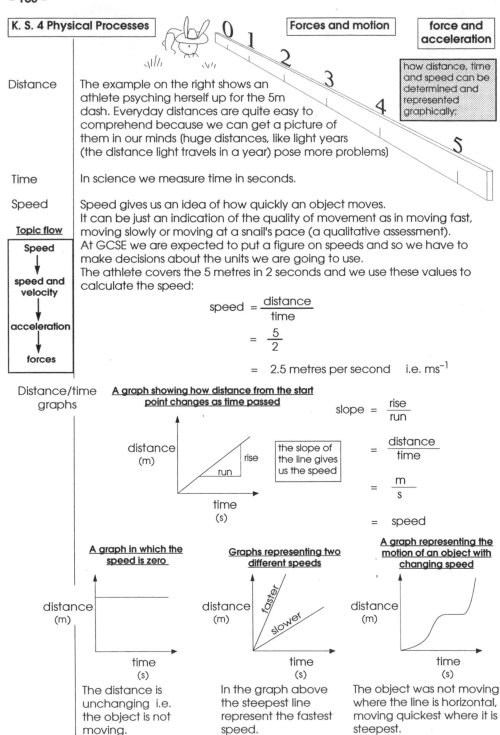

how distance, time and speed can be determined and represented graphically.

Distance

The example on the right shows an athlete psyching herself up for the 5m dash. Everyday distances are quite easy to comprehend because we can get a picture of them in our minds (huge distances, like light years (the distance light travels in a year) pose more problems)

Time

In science we measure time in seconds.

Speed

Speed gives us an idea of how quickly an object moves.
It can be just an indication of the quality of movement as in moving fast, moving slowly or moving at a snail's pace (a qualitative assessment).
At GCSE we are expected to put a figure on speeds and so we have to make decisions about the units we are going to use.
The athlete covers the 5 metres in 2 seconds and we use these values to calculate the speed:

$$\text{speed} = \frac{\text{distance}}{\text{time}}$$

$$= \frac{5}{2}$$

$$= 2.5 \text{ metres per second} \quad \text{i.e. } ms^{-1}$$

Topic flow

Speed
↓
speed and velocity
↓
acceleration
↓
forces

Distance/time graphs

A graph showing how distance from the start point changes as time passed

distance (m)

rise

run

time (s)

the slope of the line gives us the speed

$$\text{slope} = \frac{\text{rise}}{\text{run}}$$

$$= \frac{\text{distance}}{\text{time}}$$

$$= \frac{m}{s}$$

$$= \text{speed}$$

A graph in which the speed is zero

distance (m)

time (s)

The distance is unchanging i.e. the object is not moving.

Graphs representing two different speeds

distance (m)

faster

slower

time (s)

In the graph above the steepest line represent the fastest speed.

A graph representing the motion of an object with changing speed

distance (m)

time (s)

The object was not moving where the line is horizontal, moving quickest where it is steepest.

Speed/time graphs	**A general graph showing how speed changes as time passes**

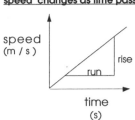

$$slope = \frac{rise}{run}$$

$$= \frac{speed}{time}$$

$$= \frac{m\,s^{-1}}{s} = m\,s^{-2}$$

$$= acceleration$$

Stopping: Four factors to consider	Breaking distance is affected by:

about factors affecting vehicle stopping distances;

1. The condition of the tyres. How much tread is left on them and are they at the correct pressure?
2. The condition of the road. Does it have a loose surface, is it wet or is there a slight covering of oil(as one would expect after a week or two without rain)?
3. The mass of the car. Is the car full of people and their luggage?
4. The speed of the vehicle. As explained below, if we double the cars speed the stopping distance will increase four times.

Losing speed

As a car speeds up it is gaining kinetic energy (energy is being transferred by the engine from fuel to the car body).

To get an idea of braking distances needed at different speeds we need to see how the total kinetic energy changes as speed increases.

Total energy and speed

Kinetic energy is given by the expression $KE = \frac{1}{2}mv^2$ — the speed at which the car is moving

To make the calculations simpler let us assume that the car has a mass of 2kg. We will now work out how much energy needs to be lost when it is travelling at $1ms^{-1}$, $2ms^{-1}$, $4ms^{-1}$, $8ms^{-1}$, $16ms^{-1}$.

The total mass of the car

16ms is about 36 mile per hour

$$KE = \frac{1}{2}mv^2 \qquad = \frac{1}{2}2v^2$$

The braking distance is proportional to the energy that must be lost.

Table showing how braking distance needed to stop the car increases as speed increases

speed of car / ms^{-1}	1	2	4	8	16
Energy that must be lost(arbitraty units) which is proportional to the braking distance	1	4	16	64	256

Speed and velocity	Velocity is speed in a stated direction. Velocity will change even when there is no change in speed provided that there is a change in direction.

the difference between speed and velocity;

| K. S. 4 Physical Processes | Forces and motion | force and acceleration | about acceleration as change in velocity per unit time; |

Acceleration   The rate of at which velocity changes

$$acceleration = \frac{change\ in\ velocity}{time\ taken\ for\ change}$$

A graph showing how speed might change with time

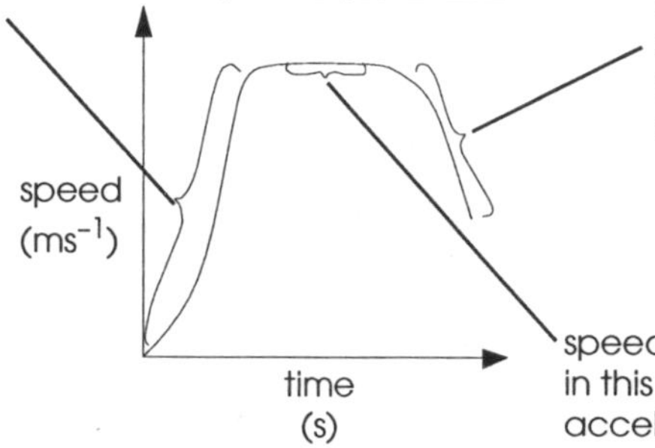

speed is increasing but not constantly i.e. acceleration is not constant (the steeper the line, the greater the acceleration).

speed (ms^{-1})

the object is slowing down, acceleration is negative

time (s)

speed is constant in this region, acceleration is zero

Summary

	Definition	Units
Speed	The rate at which something moves. Speed is given by the gradient of a distance/time graph. $$speed = \frac{distance}{time}$$	metres per second m s^{-1} (or m/s)
Velocity	This is the speed in a **stated** direction. The velocity changes even when the speed stays the same but there is change of direction.	m s^{-1} (or m/s)
Acceleration	The rate of at which velocity changes $$acceleration = \frac{change\ in\ velocity}{time\ taken\ for\ change}$$	metres per second squared m s^{-2} (or m / s^2)

Areas under curves

Another speed/time graph

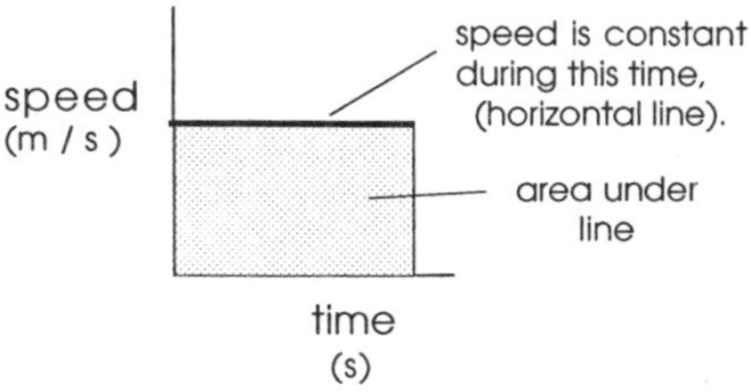

speed (m / s)

speed is constant during this time, (horizontal line).

area under line

time (s)

Deciding what the area means

follow these steps

area	=	height	x	length
	=	speed	x	time
	=	m / s	x	s
	=	m i.e. distance		

therefore the area under this graph represents the distance travelled

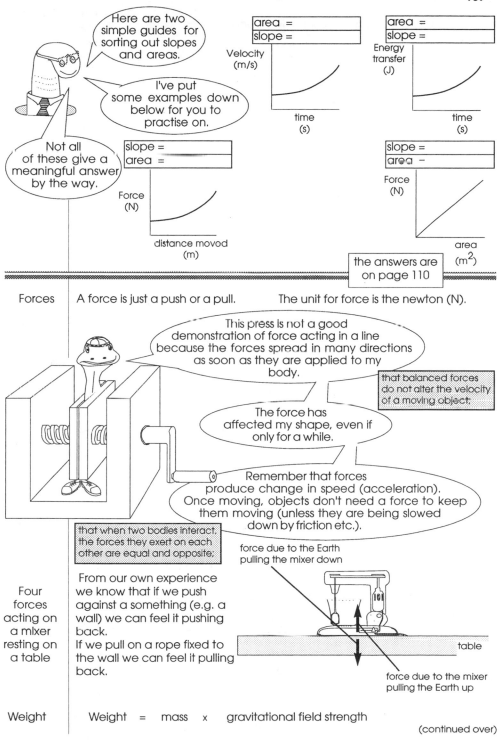

Here are two simple guides for sorting out slopes and areas.

I've put some examples down below for you to practise on.

Not all of these give a meaningful answer by the way.

area =
slope =

Velocity (m/s) vs time (s)

area =
slope =

Energy transfer (J) vs time (s)

slope =
area =

Force (N) vs distance movod (m)

slope =
area =

Force (N) vs area (m²)

the answers are on page 110

Forces A force is just a push or a pull.   The unit for force is the newton (N).

This press is not a good demonstration of force acting in a line because the forces spread in many directions as soon as they are applied to my body.

that balanced forces do not alter the velocity of a moving object;

The force has affected my shape, even if only for a while.

Remember that forces produce change in speed (acceleration). Once moving, objects don't need a force to keep them moving (unless they are being slowed down by friction etc.).

that when two bodies interact, the forces they exert on each other are equal and opposite;

Four forces acting on a mixer resting on a table

From our own experience we know that if we push against a something (e.g. a wall) we can feel it pushing back.
If we pull on a rope fixed to the wall we can feel it pulling back.

force due to the Earth pulling the mixer down

table

force due to the mixer pulling the Earth up

Weight   Weight = mass x gravitational field strength

(continued over)

K. S. 4 Physical Processes	Forces and motion	force and acceleration

Slope	
1.	acceleration
2.	power
3.	no meaning
4.	pressure

Area under the curve	
1.	distance travelled
2.	no meaning
3.	work done
4.	no meaning

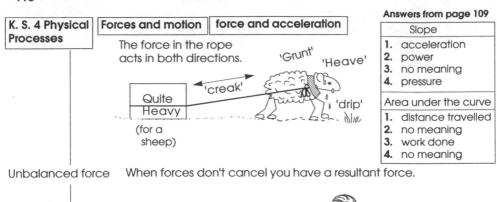

The force in the rope acts in both directions.

'Grunt' 'Heave'

'creak'

Quite Heavy

(for a sheep)

'drip'

Unbalanced force   When forces don't cancel you have a resultant force.

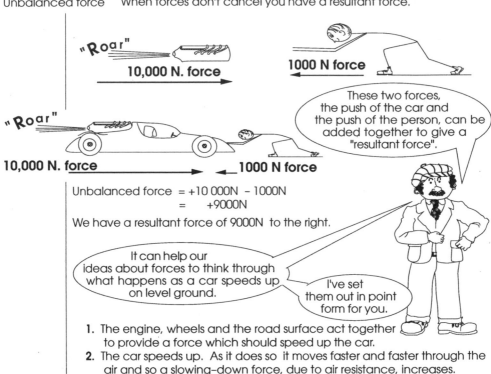

"Roar"

10,000 N. force

1000 N force

"Roar"

10,000 N. force   1000 N force

These two forces, the push of the car and the push of the person, can be added together to give a "resultant force".

Unbalanced force = +10 000N – 1000N
= +9000N

We have a resultant force of 9000N to the right.

It can help our ideas about forces to think through what happens as a car speeds up on level ground.

I've set them out in point form for you.

1. The engine, wheels and the road surface act together to provide a force which should speed up the car.
2. The car speeds up. As it does so it moves faster and faster through the air and so a slowing–down force, due to air resistance, increases.
3. When the slowing–down force matches the size of the speeding up force the car will travel at a steady speed, i.e. there is no unbalanced force acting on the car any more.

force and non-uniform motion	the forces acting on falling objects

Topic flow chart

Falling objects
↓
terminal velocity

Falling objects

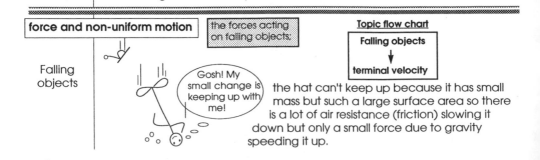

Gosh! My small change is keeping up with me!

the hat can't keep up because it has small mass but such a large surface area so there is a lot of air resistance (friction) slowing it down but only a small force due to gravity speeding it up.

| Terminal velocity | Terminal velocity is reached when the accelerating force due to gravity is the same as the slowing down force due to air resistance. Terminal velocity for the average human is about 110 miles per hour. This value can be increased or reduced by altering our shape as we fall. We can reduce it hugely be using a parachute to increase the air resistance. | why falling objects may reach a terminal velocity: |

Force, mass and acceleration

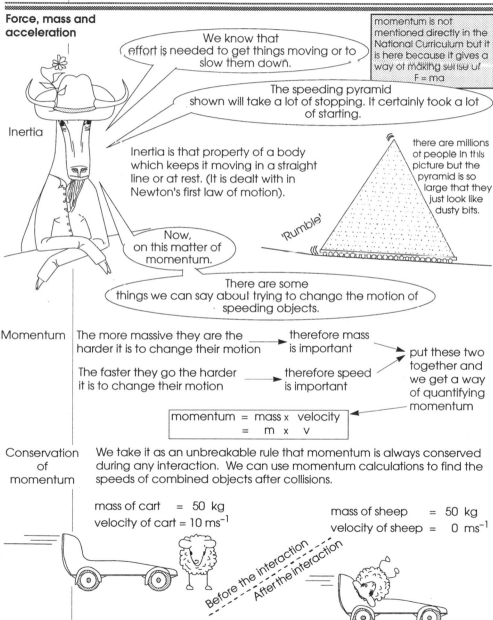

We know that effort is needed to get things moving or to slow them down.

momentum is not mentioned directly in the National Curriculum but it is here because it gives a way of making sense of F = ma

The speeding pyramid shown will take a lot of stopping. It certainly took a lot of starting.

Inertia

Inertia is that property of a body which keeps it moving in a straight line or at rest. (It is dealt with in Newton's first law of motion).

there are millions of people in this picture but the pyramid is so large that they just look like dusty bits.

'Rumble'

Now, on this matter of momentum.

There are some things we can say about trying to change the motion of speeding objects.

Momentum

The more massive they are the harder it is to change their motion ——→ therefore mass is important

The faster they go the harder it is to change their motion ——→ therefore speed is important

put these two together and we get a way of quantifying momentum

$$momentum = mass \times velocity = m \times v$$

Conservation of momentum

We take it as an unbreakable rule that momentum is always conserved during any interaction. We can use momentum calculations to find the speeds of combined objects after collisions.

mass of cart = 50 kg
velocity of cart = 10 ms^{-1}

mass of sheep = 50 kg
velocity of sheep = 0 ms^{-1}

Before the interaction

After the interaction

(the calculations are on the next page)

K. S. 4 Physical Processes

Forces and motion

Forces and non–uniform motion

total momentum before $=$ total momentum after

mv (of cart) $+$ mv (of sheep) $=$ mv (of cart + sheep)

50×10 $+$ 50×0 $=$ $(50+50) \times v$

500 $+$ 0 $=$ $100\,v$

$$\frac{500}{100} = v_{(cart + sheep)}$$

$= 5 \text{ ms-1}$

Mass

The mass of an object is the quantity of matter in the body. Objects in space may be weightless but they are not without mass.

the quantitative relationship between force, mass and acceleration;

$Ft = mv - mu$ u: initial velocity
V: final velocity

$$F = \frac{mv - mu}{t}$$

$$F = m\frac{(v - u)}{t}$$

$F = ma$

$Ft = mv - mu$

force x time
i.e. impulse

change in
momentum

$$a = \frac{(v - u)}{t}$$

acceleration

change in
velocity

$F = ma$

force (N)

mass (kg)

acceleration (ms^{-2})

O.K.!
that's enough on
acceleration, now
for some food !

The tail provides
17 N force

mass of fish is 0.75 kg

Calculating
acceleration
using
$F = ma$

While the accelerating force remains at 17 N the fish will accelerate at a certain rate which can be calculated by rearranging the equation $F = ma$

This acceleration
(22.7 m per sec faster each second)
only occurs while the overall force
remains at 17 N.

$F = ma$

therefore $\frac{F}{m} = a$

As Fish goes
faster the force due to water
resistance increases

and so $a = \frac{F}{m}$

$$a = \frac{17}{0.75}$$

so the overall force
(the net force) will be less
than 17 N

$a = 22.7 \text{ m s}^{-2}$

Try to get as much
practice at doing these calculations as
you can manage.

and the
new acceleration must
be calculated

Adding forces that act along different lines

Adding forces together	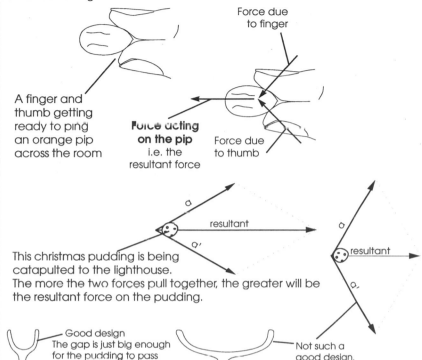

A finger and thumb getting ready to ping an orange pip across the room

Force due to finger

Force acting on the pip i.e. the resultant force

Force due to thumb

Forces as vectors	This christmas pudding is being catapulted to the lighthouse. The more the two forces pull together, the greater will be the resultant force on the pudding.

resultant

resultant

Good design
The gap is just big enough for the pudding to pass

Not such a good design.

vectors, scalars and resultants	A **vector** is any physical quantity which needs its direction to be stated in order that it be completely described e.g. velocity, force, momentum.

A **scalar** is a quantity which has only size (magnitude). Mass, volume, speed, height, distance and depth are all examples of scalar quantities.

If we add two or more vector quantities we will always get a **resultant** . The resultant of two forces is the force that will have the same effect. |

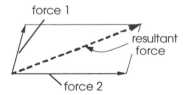

force 1

resultant force

force 2

Moments	A 'moment' is a turning force.

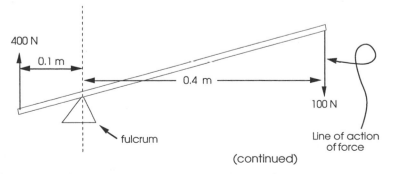

400 N

0.1 m

0.4 m

100 N

fulcrum

Line of action of force

(continued)

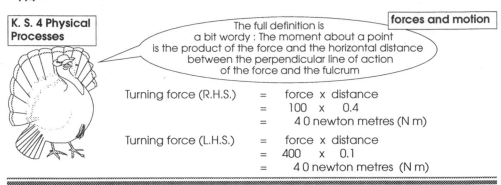

K. S. 4 Physical Processes

forces and motion

The full definition is a bit wordy : The moment about a point is the product of the force and the horizontal distance between the perpendicular line of action of the force and the fulcrum

Turning force (R.H.S.)	=	force x distance
	=	100 x 0.4
	=	4 0 newton metres (N m)
Turning force (L.H.S.)	=	force x distance
	=	400 x 0.1
	=	4 0 newton metres (N m)

---

force and pressure on solids, liquids and gases

how extension varies with applied force for a range of materials.

Hooke's Law Tension and compression and springs.

In this experiment, Celia and John are looking at the effect of increasing the force on a spring. Notice how Celia has her eyes level with the bottom of the weights (no parallax error for her). They have used the results to draw the graph shown below, and then pencilled in the effect on the metal atoms at the different stages.

Topic flow

> Hooke's law
> ↓
> liquids and pressure
> ↓
> Boyle's law

Mmmmmm ! 8 Newtons causes a .04 m extension

Look back at metallic bonds (p. 58) as this section begins by looking at what happens to the crystals in metal wire when we stretch them:
The details are summarised in the graph below.
The curve is divided into sections O to B, B to C and so on.
OB: This part is straight line though the origin. The atoms in the wire move further apart but will return to their original position if the load is removed.
BC: The crystals are beginning to slide over one another. The wire has been permanently deformed and so will not return to its original length. The wire appears to 'give' at C. If we look at the wire under a microscope we can see one or more regions where it has become 'waisted' i.e. regions where the crystals have slipped over each other and the wire has become thinner.
After D the crystal slippage is rapid and the wire breaks even though no more force is applied.

Make a note of that, John, I'll add some more weights.

Anything you say, Celia.

A graph showing how extension is affected by load on a length of spring

Hooke's law: Provided that we do not exceed the elastic limit of the material, the deformation of a material is proportional to the force applied to it.

At the **elastic limit** atoms begin to rearrange i.e. any further extension becomes permanent.

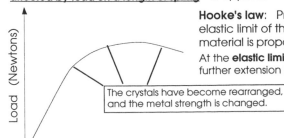

The crystals have become rearranged, and the metal strength is changed.

It is more common to present this information as a stress/strain graph. (but we don't need to bother with that at GCSE level)

Load (Newtons)

0   Extension (cm)

$$stress = \frac{force}{area} \qquad strain = \frac{extension}{original\ length}$$

A graph showing how extension is affected by load for a brittle material and for a ductile material

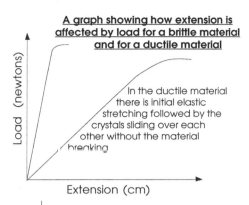

Load (newtons) / Extension (cm)

In the ductile material there is initial elastic stretching followed by the crystals sliding over each other without the material breaking

A graph showing how extension is affected by load for a rubber band

Load (newtons) / Extension (cm)

changes during stretching

changes during contraction

A graph showing how extension is affected by load for a piece of polythene

Load (newtons) / Extension (cm)

loading

unloading

Brittle material	The brittle material needs a lot of force for a small extension and then suddenly snaps.
Rubber band	One way of interpreting what is happening when the elastic band stretches and then returns to its original length is that it costs us more effort to stretch it than we get back when it contracts. The difference between the two will be the work we must do.
Polythene	In the case of the polythene, the chains of atoms slide over each other so that it will not return to its original length even though only a fairly small force has been applied.

| Pressure, volume and temperature | When particles bounce against each other, a force is produced. This force is spread over the area involved in the bouncing. | how liquids behave under pressure including simple everyday applications of hydraulics. |

| pascal | Pressure $= \dfrac{\text{force}}{\text{area}}$ (the units might therefore be newtons per metre^2) (1 pascal = 1 newton per metre^2) |

| Hydraulics | 1. Particles in a liquid are close together and so it is hard to force them much closer.
2. Pressure in a liquid acts in all directions.

Liquids are therefore fairly incompressible and so we can use them to transfer forces through tubes.

We can think of hydraulics in the same way that we think of other force multipliers like car jacks or crow bars; on the effort side we move a fairly small force through a large distance and this results in a much larger force being moved through a small distance at the load. |

| A simple hydraulic system (without a return valve) | a large force is delivered by this piston

Hydraulic fluid
because of the way pressure is transmitted equally in all directions it gets around the corners |

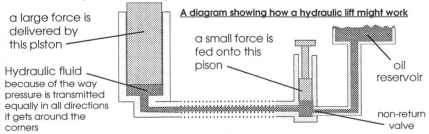

A diagram showing how a hydraulic lift might work

a small force is fed onto this pison

oil reservoir

non-return valve

K. S. 4 Physical Processes	Forces and motion	how the volume of a fixed mass of gas at constant temperature is related to pressure.
	force and pressure on solids, liquids and gases	

Boyle's law

If we increase the pressure on a gas, the volume will get smaller.
At constant temperature, the volume of a fixed mass of gas is inversely proportional to the pressure.

If we double the pressure, we halve the volume.

If we treble the pressure the volume reduces to a third and so on.

All of this can be set out as a formula: $p_1V_1 = p_2V_2$

A worked example

A 50 cm³ gas bubble rises from 10 m depth to the surface. The temperature does not change. What is the volume (V_2) of the bubble at the surface ? (pressure at 10 m is 2 atmospheres)

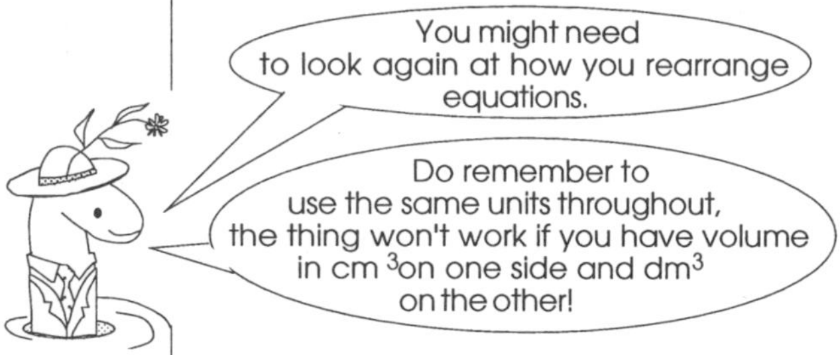

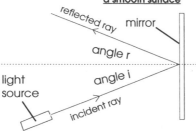

You might need to look again at how you rearrange equations.

Do remember to use the same units throughout, the thing won't work if you have volume in cm³ on one side and dm³ on the other!

initial values / final values

$$p_1V_1 = p_2V_2$$

$$2 \times 50 = 1 \times V_2$$

$$\frac{2 \times 50}{1} = V_2$$

$$V_2 = 100 \ cm^3$$

Waves | **characteristics of waves** | that light and sound can be reflected, refracted and diffracted;

Reflection

The term reflection is used to cover the events that take place when waves or particles bounce. The bouncing takes place at the junction between two different substances e.g. at the junction of air and water, air and the silver film on a mirror or a rigid board.

Normal

The normal, shown in the diagrams, is an imaginary line at right angles to the surface at a point.

Topic flow

Light and sound
↓
waves along a spring
↓
more waves
↓
frequency, wave length and amplitude
↓
energy transfer

Diagram showing light and sound bouncing off a smooth surface

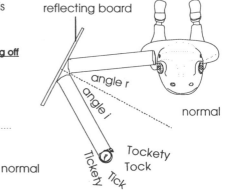

reflecting board

angle r

angle i

normal

reflected ray   mirror

angle r

light source

angle i

incident ray

normal

Tockety Tock

Tickety Tick

Light from the light source bounces against the mirror in such a way that the angle of incidence (angle i) is always equal to the angle of reflection(angle r). (Normal, incident ray and reflected ray are all in the same plane)
The sound from the pocket watch behaves in much the same way.

Refraction

Refraction refers to the change in direction that takes place when waves or particles change their speed.

In the case of light there is a change of speed as the light passes from one medium to another (e.g. from water to air). In this case the light ray bends away from the normal.

Moving particles will also show refraction when they change their speed.

Refraction taking place at the air/water interface (light) and air/carbon dioxide junction (sound)

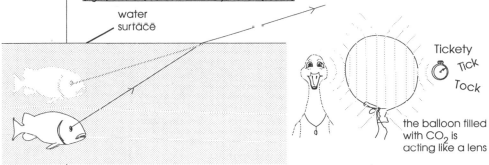

water surface

Tickety

Tick

Tock

the balloon filled with CO_2 is acting like a lens

The fish appears to be higher than it really is because the light bends as it leaves the water (and because our brains can not take this into account).

It is quite difficult to get the balloon to act as a lens in the lab. (perhaps because there is so much stray noise)

Diffraction

Both light and sound spread out after passing an obstacle. For example, light spreads out from a pinhole to fill the space beyond and we can hear people talking in the next room through a crack (the walls are much too thick to act as a sounding board).

This spreading out of waves is referred to as diffraction (see page 118).

Internal reflection
(continued)
(see critical angle on page 120)

Light entering fine glass fibres will keep bouncing down the fibre unable to escape.

the conditions for total internal reflection and its use in optical fibres.

By packing a lot of fine glass fibres together side by side and fitting a lens system at each end, we can make a flexible fibre optic device.

A diagram showing the main features of fibre optic systems

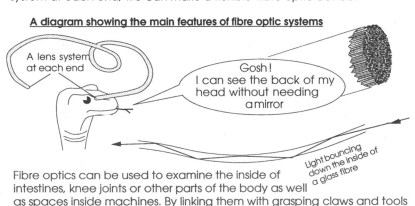

A lens system at each end

Gosh! I can see the back of my head without needing a mirror

Light bouncing down the inside of a glass fibre

Fibre optics can be used to examine the inside of intestines, knee joints or other parts of the body as well as spaces inside machines. By linking them with grasping claws and tools they have made 'keyhole surgery' possible.

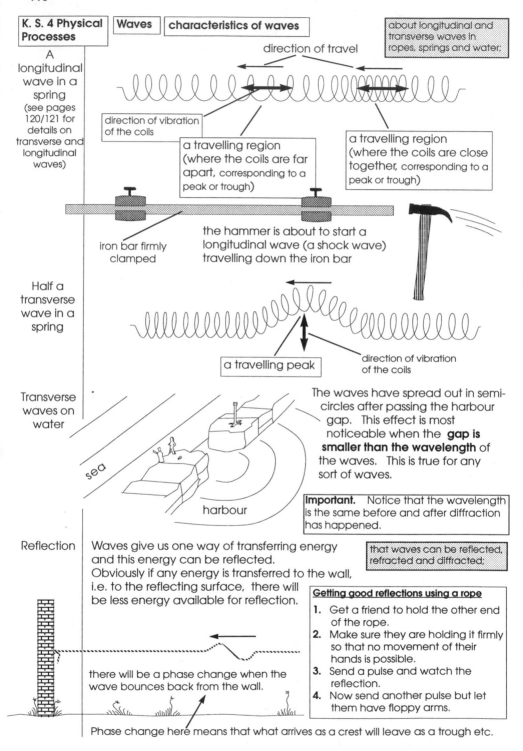

K. S. 4 Physical Processes | **Waves** | **characteristics of waves**

about longitudinal and transverse waves in ropes, springs and water;

A longitudinal wave in a spring (see pages 120/121 for details on transverse and longitudinal waves)

direction of travel

direction of vibration of the coils

a travelling region (where the coils are far apart, corresponding to a peak or trough)

a travelling region (where the coils are close together, corresponding to a peak or trough)

iron bar firmly clamped

the hammer is about to start a longitudinal wave (a shock wave) travelling down the iron bar

Half a transverse wave in a spring

a travelling peak

direction of vibration of the coils

Transverse waves on water

The waves have spread out in semi-circles after passing the harbour gap. This effect is most noticeable when the **gap is smaller than the wavelength** of the waves. This is true for any sort of waves.

sea

harbour

Important. Notice that the wavelength is the same before and after diffraction has happened.

Reflection

Waves give us one way of transferring energy and this energy can be reflected. Obviously if any energy is transferred to the wall, i.e. to the reflecting surface, there will be less energy available for reflection.

that waves can be reflected, refracted and diffracted;

Getting good reflections using a rope

1. Get a friend to hold the other end of the rope.
2. Make sure they are holding it firmly so that no movement of their hands is possible.
3. Send a pulse and watch the reflection.
4. Now send another pulse but let them have floppy arms.

there will be a phase change when the wave bounces back from the wall.

Phase change here means that what arrives as a crest will leave as a trough etc.

Refraction

A diagram showing a ripple tank from above

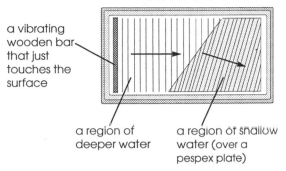

a vibrating wooden bar that just touches the surface

a region of deeper water

a region of shallow water (over a pespex plate)

Things to note

1. The waves change direction as they pass into the shallow water.
2. They slow down as they move into the shallow water.
3. The wavelength gets shorter.
4. **But the frequency does not change.**

A diagram showing the same ripple tank from above but this time with a barrier having a small hole in it

Diffraction

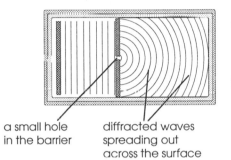

a small hole in the barrier

diffracted waves spreading out across the surface

Things to note

1. For the best effect the hole should be smaller than the wavelength
2. The wavelength does not change after passing the barrier.

The speed of light

In a vacuum, light of different wavelengths has the same speed i.e. 300 million metres per second. ($2.997\,925 \times 10^8$ m s^{-1} to be exact) Out of a vacuum, the different wavelengths (e.g. the different colours or wavelengths of radio waves) travel at a different speeds so that some fall increasingly behind others (i.e. dispersion occurs).

Three diagrams showing light being reflected or refracted

Reflection of light

Both waves and particles are reflected from surfaces in a predictable way. When you draw the diagram showing how an image is formed in a mirror, it is important to draw it in the right order.

1. Draw the mirror.
2. Draw the object.
3. Draw the image as far behind the mirror as the object is in front of it.
4. Draw in the eye on the same side as the object.
5. Draw two lines from the image to the pupil.
6. Now link up the object with the points where the lines pass through the mirror.
7. Don't forget to fill in the arrow-heads.

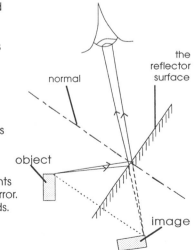

the reflector surface

normal

object

image

Refraction of light

i = angle of incidence
r = angle of refraction

air

glass block

air

air

air

air

i

r

incident ray

refracted rays

Refraction (bending) occurs at each interface i.e. where air and glass meet

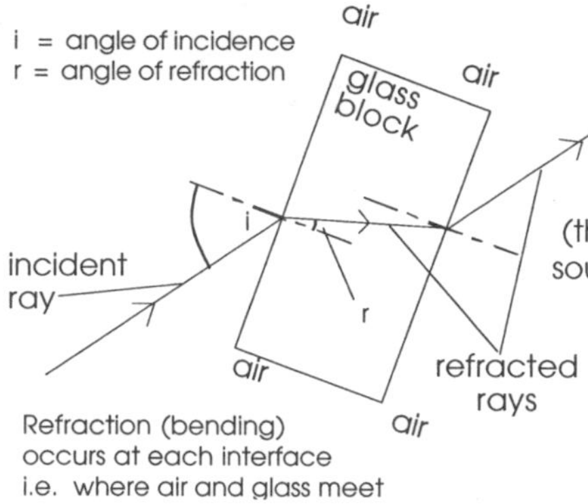

Waves change direction when they change their speed, e.g. light rays bend as they pass through a prism. Sound will refract as it passes from cold air to warm air (this is part of the explanation of why sound travels so well over water).

Light travels more slowly in glass than in air.

Critical angles
(have a look back at the bottom of page 117)

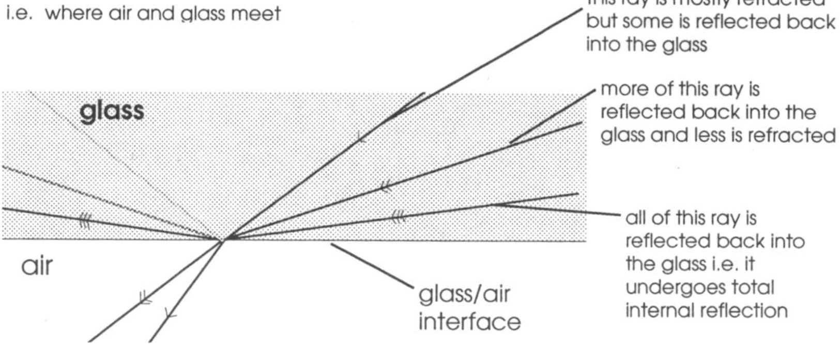

glass

air

glass/air interface

this ray is mostly refracted but some is reflected back into the glass

more of this ray is reflected back into the glass and less is refracted

all of this ray is reflected back into the glass i.e. it undergoes total internal reflection

The critical angle is the smallest angle of incidence at which total internal reflection occurs.

A summary of the main features of transverse and longitudinal waves

Transverse Waves
e.g. light waves, some earthquake waves or waves on the surface of water

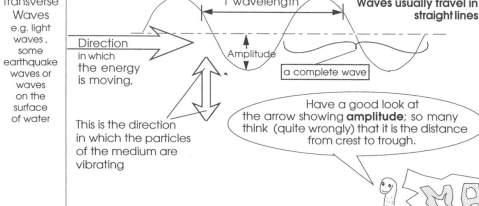

1 wavelength

Direction in which the energy is moving,

Amplitude

a complete wave

This is the direction in which the particles of the medium are vibrating

Waves usually travel in straight lines.

Have a good look at the arrow showing **amplitude**; so many think (quite wrongly) that it is the distance from crest to trough.

Longitudinal waves
e.g. sound waves in air or shock waves in water or the earth.

The dots represent molecules: in nature they are not as regularly placed as this, except in crystals.

1 wavelength

This is the direction in which the particles of the medium are vibrating

region where the molecules are closest together

region where the molecules are furthest apart

the meaning of frequency, wavelength and amplitude of a wave:

Frequency — The rate at which "complete waves" pass a point is the frequency. If 10 waves pass each second then the frequency is 10 cycles/sec. i.e. 10 Hz.

hertz — One hertz = one cycle /sec.

Velocity — The wave's speed = frequency x wavelength. The speed of a wave is the distance that it travels in one second.

$$v = f \times \lambda$$

velocity / wave length
frequency

Amplitude — This gives us an idea of the energy being carried by the waves. Think of waves on the sea. Tall waves mean lots of energy, i.e. DANGER!

the quantitative relationship between the speed, frequency and wavelength of a wave;

Use the formula $v = f\lambda$ to complete the table of radio frequencies and wavelengths.

Channel	frequencies	Wavelengths
Radio 1	99.2 MHz and 1089 kHz	
Radio 4	94.1 MHz and 198 kHz	
Radio 5	909 kHz	

The velocity of light is about 3×10^8 m s^{-1}

the answers are on the next page.

that waves transfer energy without transferring matter;

Waves are a way of transferring energy.

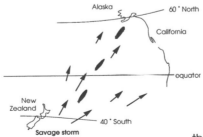

In the seventies, oceanographers set up an excellent experiment. They used ships in the Pacific along with recording stations near islands and tracked the waves that were generated by a savage southern storm in the ocean south of New Zealand.

The waves were found to travel right across the Pacific, at last transferring the remaining energy on the beaches of Alaska.

(continued (briefly))

K. S. 4 Physical Processes	Waves	**characteristics of waves**

(continued from page 121)

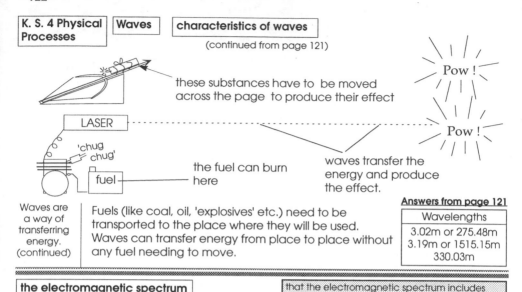

these substances have to be moved across the page to produce their effect

Pow !

LASER

Pow !

'chug chug'

the fuel can burn here

fuel

waves transfer the energy and produce the effect.

Waves are a way of transferring energy. (continued)	Fuels (like coal, oil, 'explosives' etc.) need to be transported to the place where they will be used. Waves can transfer energy from place to place without any fuel needing to move.

Answers from page 121

Wavelengths
3.02m or 275.48m
3.19m or 1515.15m
330.03m

---

the electromagnetic spectrum

that the electromagnetic spectrum includes radio waves, microwaves, infra-red, visible light, ultraviolet waves, X-rays and gamma rays;

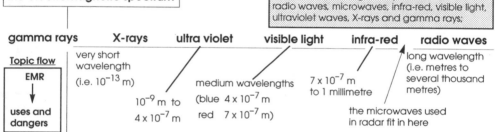

gamma rays   **X-rays**   **ultra violet**   **visible light**   **infra-red**   **radio waves**

Topic flow

EMR

↓

uses and dangers

very short wavelength (i.e. 10^{-13} m)

10^{-9} m to 4×10^{-7} m

medium wavelengths (blue 4×10^{-7} m red 7×10^{-7} m)

7×10^{-7} m to 1 millimetre

long wavelength (i.e. metres to several thousand metres)

the microwaves used in radar fit in here

The electro-magnetic spectrum (i.e. the EMR family)	Electromagnetic radiation (EMR) is composed of waves of energy that are produced when charged particles accelerate (as happens when electrons accelerate during lightning which is why the radio crackles). Unlike other waves of our experience, e.g. sound, earthquake waves, or the waves on water, **EMR can travel through a vacuum.** EMR is composed of electric and magnetic fields vibrating at right angles to each other. EMR usually behaves as though it is composed of waves (e.g. during refraction, reflection, diffraction and interference) but during the photo-electric effect (when light knocks electrons from certain atoms e.g. zinc) light seems to behave like a stream of particles. The best description of these waves is a mathematical one (Maxwell's equations), but we don't need to bother with this at GCSE.
Evidence that light travels as waves	If light travels as waves then it should show the properties of waves. Your work with ripple tanks will have shown that waves refract and that when they pass from deep water to shallow water they refract towards the normal. Measurements of their speed shows that they slow down as the water gets shallower. Light refracts towards the normal as it passes from air to glass and it slows down as it passes into the glass. (To get the path of moving particles to bend towards the normal we have to speed them up; you may remember the iron ball rolling down the slope covered with carbon paper)

| EMR. and its uses | some uses and dangers of microwaves, infra-red and ultraviolet waves in domestic situations; some uses of radio waves, microwaves, infra-red and visible light in communications; |||

some uses of X-rays and gamma-rays in medicine;

Radiation	Uses
Radio waves	Radio–astronomy, radio and television broadcasting, radar, microwave ovens, longer distance telephone links.
Infra red	Heat treatment of damaged muscle; cameras that can see in the dark because of the infra-red radiated from all warm objects (bodies, compost heaps, the ground etc.), remote controls for T.V.s etc.
Ultra–violet	Has a strong bactericidal action and so is used to sterilise operating theatres. It causes certain substances to fluoresce (glow) so it has forensic uses, helping people to find fingerprints and stains. It is used inside fluorescent lamps and causes the fluorescent powders on the inside of the glass to glow brightly. **UV damages eyesight** and should never be viewed directly.
X–rays	X-rays penetrate flesh more readily than they do bone, and so can be used to look at the structure of bones and internal organs. In order to keep the doses of X-rays as low as possible the film is now placed between two sheets of glass which have been coated with a material that fluoresces brightly when X-rays strike it. Short wavelength X-rays are used to bombard cancerous tissue. In industry X-rays can be used to check for cracks in welds and cast metal objects.
Gamma rays	Gamma rays are a very penetrating type of radiation, used to check for cracks in metal structures. They kill bacteria and so can be used to sterilise food so that the shelf–life is greatly increased or sterilise equipment like syringes, needles etc.

sound and ultrasound

about sound and ultrasound waves, and some medical and other uses of ultrasound;

Sound	Sound shows all the properties of waves (except polarisation). It travels by means of longitudinal waves and cannot pass through a vacuum. (waves that are polarised all vibrate in the same plane.)

The sound spectrum

a weak thudding sound   speech   high notes   hiss   ultrasound

frequency: 20Hz
wavelength: 6 m

frequency: 20000Hz
wavelength: 0.0165 m

Middle C fits in here
frequency: 256Hz
wavelength: 1.26 m

Sound levels

We measure noise levels in decibels. One decibel represents an increase of sound intensity of about 26%. This is the smallest change which the average human ear can detect.

(continued)

Sound	dB level
threshold of hearing	0
whispering	30
normal conversation	60
busy street	70
noisy factory	90
jet plane overhead	100
loud thunderclap	110
threshold of pain	120

| K. S. 4 Physical Processes | Waves | sound and ultrasound | (continued from the last page) |

Loudness and pitch

The loudness of the sound depends on the amplitude of the sound waves. The pitch of the sound (whether the note is high or low) depends on the frequency.

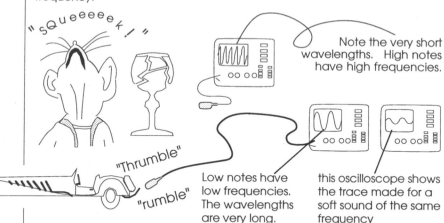

"sQueeeeek!"

Note the very short wavelengths. High notes have high frequencies.

"Thrumble"

"rumble"

Low notes have low frequencies. The wavelengths are very long.

this oscilloscope shows the trace made for a soft sound of the same frequency

Uses of ultrasound

Sound waves reflect from smooth surfaces. Reflection will occur at the junction of one tissue and another e.g. we can get a reflection from the kidneys inside the body. The ultrasound will also be reflected by cracks in metal objects or by shoals of fish or the bed of the lake or sea.

1. Ultrasound is pulsed into the body. The echoes are collected, analysed and presented as a picture showing the shape and size of the internal organs. It gives us a very useful way of examining the unborn child so that doctors can check that development is normal. The ultrasound has very low energy levels so that damage to tissues is negligible but it should nevertheless not be overused (it is not a toy).

2. Ultrasound devices can be used to measure short distances e.g. used by carpet fitters to measure the size of a room without having to scrabble about on hands and knees with a tape measure.

3. On a small scale it can be used to check for flaws in metal objects or, on a much larger scale, it can be bounced off shoals of fish or the sea bed and so used to locate a catch or survey the sea bed.

that longitudinal and transverse waves are transmitted through the Earth, producing wave records that provide evidence for the Earth's layered structure.

seismic waves

Topic flow

Earth
↓
more
Earth

Three wave types spread out from earthquakes. Two are transverse waves and have been labelled the surface wave and the S wave. The third is a longitudinal wave known as the P wave. Because P waves are shock waves they can spread through a liquid and so will travel through the centre of the Earth.

The diagram on the right shows these three wave types spreading out from an earthquake. They follow curved paths because the density of the rock keeps changing and so their speed keeps changing (i.e. they keep refracting).

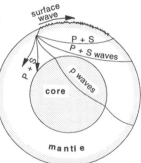

surface wave

P + S
P + S waves

P + S

P waves

core

mantle

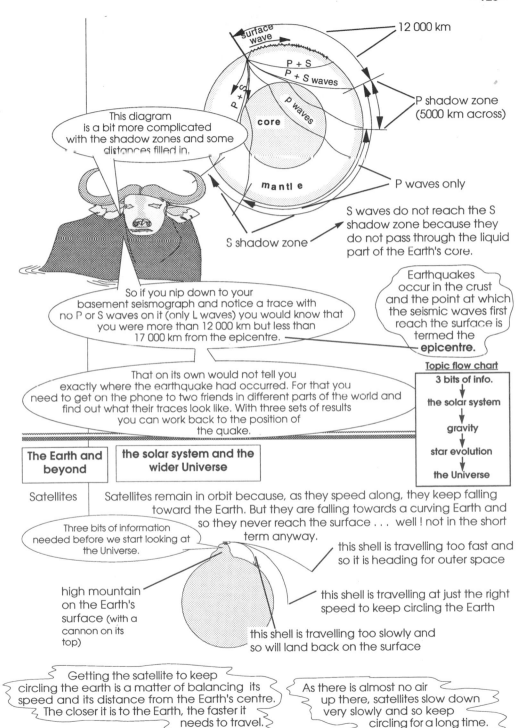

12 000 km

P shadow zone (5000 km across)

surface wave

P + S
P + S waves

core

p waves

mantle

P waves only

S waves do not reach the S shadow zone because they do not pass through the liquid part of the Earth's core.

This diagram is a bit more complicated with the shadow zones and some distances filled in.

S shadow zone

So if you nip down to your basement seismograph and notice a trace with no P or S waves on it (only L waves) you would know that you were more than 12 000 km but less than 17 000 km from the epicentre.

Earthquakes occur in the crust and the point at which the seismic waves first reach the surface is termed the **epicentre.**

That on its own would not tell you exactly where the earthquake had occurred. For that you need to get on the phone to two friends in different parts of the world and find out what their traces look like. With three sets of results you can work back to the position of the quake.

Topic flow chart

3 bits of info.
↓
the solar system
↓
gravity
↓
star evolution
↓
the Universe

The Earth and beyond	the solar system and the wider Universe

Satellites

Satellites remain in orbit because, as they speed along, they keep falling toward the Earth. But they are falling towards a curving Earth and so they never reach the surface . . . well ! not in the short term anyway.

Three bits of information needed before we start looking at the Universe.

this shell is travelling too fast and so it is heading for outer space

high mountain on the Earth's surface (with a cannon on its top)

this shell is travelling at just the right speed to keep circling the Earth

this shell is travelling too slowly and so will land back on the surface

Getting the satellite to keep circling the earth is a matter of balancing its speed and its distance from the Earth's centre. The closer it is to the Earth, the faster it needs to travel.

As there is almost no air up there, satellites slow down very slowly and so keep circling for a long time.

that gravitational forces determine the movement of planets, moons, comets and satellites;

Gravity

Gravity is the name given to the attractive force that exists between any two objects. The force will be greatest between large, dense objects that are close together.

Newton's **law of universal gravitation** states that any two particles of matter attract one another with a force which is proportional to the product of their masses and inversely proportional to the square of their distances apart.

If this sounds like so much gibberish to you, take it a bit at a time.

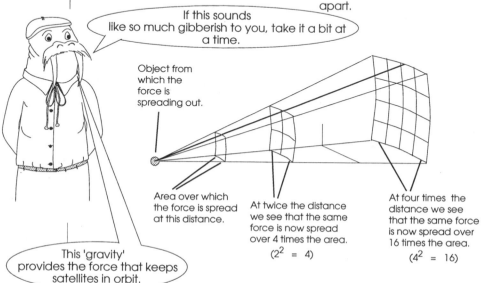

Object from which the force is spreading out.

Area over which the force is spread at this distance.

At twice the distance we see that the same force is now spread over 4 times the area. ($2^2 = 4$)

At four times the distance we see that the same force is now spread over 16 times the area. ($4^2 = 16$)

This 'gravity' provides the force that keeps satellites in orbit.

Doppler shift
(see also red shift page 129)

This is the apparent change in the frequency of of light or sound caused because the source is speeding towards or away from us. Most commonly we know of it because of the changing note of the sirens on moving vehicles.

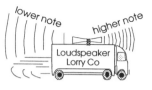

lower note

higher note

Loudspeaker Lorry Co

the truck is speeding in this direction

Between each pulse from the speaker the truck has moved a little further along the road and so the pulses travelling forward are closer together.

The significance to astronomy

Light from bright objects like stars or galaxies that are speeding away from us will appear more red than it should be. We can use the amount of shift to give us an idea of how fast these objects are speeding away from us.

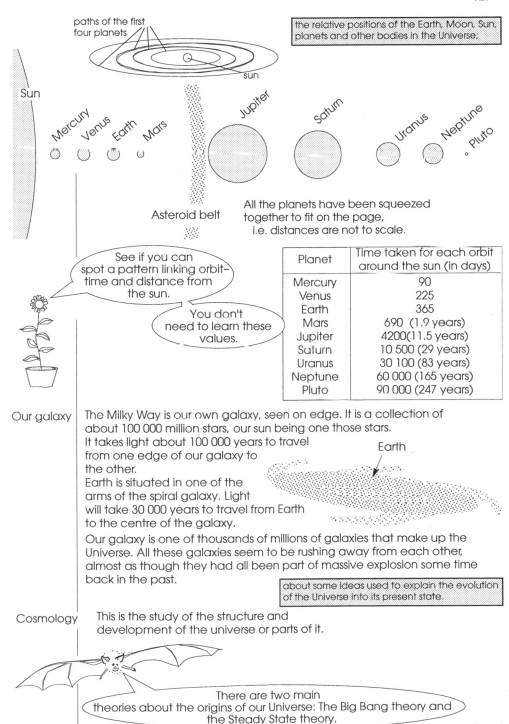

paths of the first
four planets

the relative positions of the Earth, Moon, Sun,
planets and other bodies in the Universe.

sun

Sun

Mercury Venus Earth Mars Jupiter Saturn Uranus Neptune Pluto

Asteroid belt

All the planets have been squeezed
together to fit on the page,
i.e. distances are not to scale.

See if you can
spot a pattern linking orbit-
time and distance from
the sun.

You don't
need to learn these
values.

Planet	Time taken for each orbit around the sun (in days)
Mercury	90
Venus	225
Earth	365
Mars	690 (1.9 years)
Jupiter	4200 (11.5 years)
Saturn	10 500 (29 years)
Uranus	30 100 (83 years)
Neptune	60 000 (165 years)
Pluto	90 000 (247 years)

Our galaxy

The Milky Way is our own galaxy, seen on edge. It is a collection of
about 100 000 million stars, our sun being one those stars.
It takes light about 100 000 years to travel
from one edge of our galaxy to
the other.
Earth is situated in one of the
arms of the spiral galaxy. Light
will take 30 000 years to travel from Earth
to the centre of the galaxy.

Earth

Our galaxy is one of thousands of millions of galaxies that make up the
Universe. All these galaxies seem to be rushing away from each other,
almost as though they had all been part of massive explosion some time
back in the past.

about some ideas used to explain the evolution
of the Universe into its present state.

Cosmology

This is the study of the structure and
development of the universe or parts of it.

There are two main
theories about the origins of our Universe: The Big Bang theory and
the Steady State theory.

(continued)

K. S. 4 Physical Processes	The Earth and beyond	the solar system and the wider Universe

The Big Bang theory (Super dense theory)

This suggests that our Universe has not always existed, it began about 15×10^{-9} years ago (between 10 and 20 thousand million) during a pretty spectacular explosion.

At the time of the explosion all the matter in the Universe was concentrated into the space of a single atomic nucleus.

In the first 10^{-36} seconds the basic structure of matter was decided.

Within 3 minutes nuclei of the lighter elements were beginning to form (e.g. helium and lithium).

At about 100 000 years after the start, matter and radiation began to separate. The matter grew to form the present stars, planets, galaxies, and background matter. The radiation has spread out to give the background radiation that can be detected today.

The evidence

1. According to the theory the Universe ought to be still expanding and this seems to be be the case. All the galaxies can be shown to be moving away from each other. The furthest galaxies are moving away the fastest (see 'red shift' on the next page). (this is exactly the effect we would expect if the whole universe was expanding)

2. From the theory we would expect there still to be background radiation from the original explosion and this has now been detected. There is a problem though in that it seems to be constant from every direction whereas we would expect it to be stronger from the direction of the first explosion.

3. The theory predicts that there should be light elements spread through space and this does seem to be the case.

Some difficulties

1. The theory does not give any idea about the state of things before the big bang.

2. It seems to suggest that the present laws of physics have only applied since the initial explosion.

3. The background radiation should not be the same intensity from every direction and yet this seems to be the case (recent measurements from space probes may have detected ripples in the background but more evidence needs to be collected).

4. It has been suggested that the age of our Universe, given by the big bang theory, is too small (the galaxies may have needed longer to form).

5. Quasars (quasi–stellar objects), which radiate very intensely, don't seem to fit into the big bang theory very easily.

The Steady State theory

The Universe has always existed and will continue to exist in its present form. Because there is no doubt that the Universe is expanding and because it is felt that the density of the Universe should remain the same, the theory suggests that matter is being created all the time in the spaces appearing between the galaxies. Calculations show that matter needs to be created at the rate of 10^{-43} kg m^{-3} s^{-1} .

mass of matter · per volume of space · per time

The evidence and difficulties | The steady state theory gives another explanation for the history of our Universe which takes account of the inconsistencies in the big bang theory, mentioned on the previous page.

The difficulties arise because, in order to explain all the observations, the theory has had to become quite complicated and scientists become uneasy as explanations become more complicated. They prefer to support the simplest theory that explains the known facts.

Red shift and the expanding Universe | If we look at any of the galaxies around us they seem to be moving away from our galaxy. Those galaxies which are furthest away seem to be moving away the fastest. The relationship between recessional velocity and distance away is fairly constant and is know as the 'Hubble constant'

speed at which the galaxy is moving away

$$\text{Hubble constant (H)} = \frac{\text{recessional velocity}}{\text{distance away}}$$

not really a true constant as the value can vary depending on which object is being studied.

$$- \quad 50 - 100 \text{ km s}^{-1} \text{ per 3.26 million light years}$$

a light year is the distance travelled by light in one year. $(9.4607 \times 10^{15} \text{ metres})$

It seemed reasonable for astronomers to assume that all galaxies would give out the same colours of light. When they looked at them however, they found that, as galaxies got further and further away from us, there was a measurable shift in their light towards the red end of the spectrum (towards light with a longer wavelength).

Hubble's constant and the age of the Universe |

The simplest explanation of this red shift is that it results when light is emitted from objects that are moving away from us (in the same way that ambulance sirens make a lower sound as the ambulance moves away).

If we assume that the expansion of the Universe is due to an initial explosion we can work back to it's age from the Hubble's constant.

Let us put in the units and then simplify:

$$\text{Hubble's constant} = \frac{\text{recessional velocity}}{\text{distance away}}$$

$$= \frac{\text{m s}^{-1}}{\text{m}}$$

$$= \text{s}^{-1} \quad = \frac{1}{s}$$

Using this method, we get an upper limit for the age of the Universe at 20 thousand million years (20×10^9 years).

The birth and death of stars |
1. Stars form within clouds of dust and gas in space.
2. The material collects because the gravity of the growing mass attracts more dust to it.

how stars evolve over a long time scale;

3. The dust and bits accelerate towards the growing star, crashing violently into it and raising its temperature.
4. The star begins to glow when the temperature is high enough to allow hydrogen atoms to fuse into helium atoms. When this happens huge amounts of energy are released.
(The temperature needed is of the order of 10^8 K)

(continued)

K. S. 4 Physical Processes	The Earth and beyond	the solar system and the wider Universe

The birth and death of stars (continued)

5. The stream of radiation and particles spread out from the centre of the star and prevent is from collapsing. As long as the hydrogen to helium fusion continues, the star will remain much the same size.
6. With time the mass of the star decreases, its gravity field decreases in strength and so material is pushed further out from the centre i.e. the star becomes a giant.
7. At the same time it gives off light containing longer wavelengths i.e. it has become a **red giant**. Such a star has virtually run out of the hydrogen needed to sustain the nuclear reaction.
8. There is now much less radiation streaming out and so the star collapses forming a **white dwarf**.
9. Very massive stars may undergo several cycles of getting larger and smaller.
10. But finally, the star may explode (the exploding star is a **supernova**), throwing off the outer layer of dust into space. The core has now formed an extremely dense **neutron star**.
11. Second generation stars (e.g. the sun) are formed in the dust and gas from exploding supernovas.

Topic flow chart

Energy resources and energy transfer	energy transfer	that differences in temperature can lead to transfer of energy;

how energy is transferred by the movement of particles in conduction, convection and evaporation

Energy transfer
↓
conduction, convection and evaporation
↓
radiation
↓
insulation
↓
efficiency

Energy conduction in solids

Thermal energy is conducted differently through metals and non–metals.

In the hot region of a metal, free electrons gain energy; they move faster, and they drift into cooler parts of the metal. There is a drift of electrons with less energy in the opposite direction.

These same free electrons are involved in the conduction of electricity, and so it is not really surprising that good electrical conductors are almost always good heat conductors.

A certain amount of energy is also conducted because the particles in the hot region are vibrating more vigorously and this vibrational energy is passed along the object.

Metal rod

GloW

crashing electrons

crashing electrons

sssSSSsssiH   HissSSSsss

Conduction in liquids

Most liquids are very poor conductors of energy. The energy is passed on from one particle to the next during collisions so that it moves away from hot regions of the liquid to cooler regions. This usually happens very slowly.

Showing that water is a poor conductor of heat

the water boils at the top of the tube yet the ice does not melt

Ice weighted down with gauze

Convection | During convection, energy is carried through the liquid by movement in the liquid or gas itself (rather than by vibration of the individual molecules).

The liquid gets hot near the bottom, where the heat is being applied. It expands and so becomes less dense and so the hotter fluid rises. The space is then filled with cooler liquid from above and the process is repeated.

convection currents

Convection will take place in any gas or liquid, (it is the process by which the upstairs radiators keep warm even when the pump is off).

Evaporation

heat

An explanation for the observation that evaporation cools

1. A liquid is composed of particles which are all on the move.
2. Of these particles, some will be moving quickly, others will be moving slowly.
3. It is the faster particles which will have the energy needed to leave the surface. When they do this they will carry their energy with them i.e. the liquid will get cooler.

Thermocouple

how energy is transferred by radiation.

A diagram showing the main features of a thermocouple
(this gives us one way to measure radiant heat)

hot junction

heat

G — sensitive ammeter (galvanometer)

cold junction

wires of two different metals

reference temperature

Radiation | Energy can also be lost from hot objects as a stream of light and other electromagnetic waves (e.g. infra-red) . We call this sort of energy transfer 'radiation'.

Dull black objects radiate well.

Shiny white objects are poor radiators.

Joining several hot junctions to make a more sensitive thermocouple (a thermopile)

bismuth

antimony

Thermopile | By joining several thermocouples in series we can increase the sensitivity to the thermocouple. Such a device is known as a thermopile.

Using a thermopile to compare the amount of energy radiated by kettles with different surfaces (the different items in the diagram are not to scale)

the other kettles (with different surfaces) are still in the cupboard and will be used later to test the effect of surface texture on radiation

a shiny kettle filled with very hot water
(the spout is towards us and so it doesn't look much like a kettle)

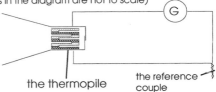

the thermopile

G

the reference couple

As radiation spreads out in all directions it will get weaker in the same way that gravity or electric fields get weaker i.e. it obeys the inverse square rule.

We could use this equipment to check this.

- 132 -

K. S. 4 Physical Processes	Energy resources and energy transfer	energy transfer

that insulation can reduce transfer of energy from hotter to colder objects, and how insulation is used in domestic contexts;

Reducing heat loss

When we attempt to reduce energy transfer, we have to keep all three ways of energy transfer (conduction, convection and radiation) in mind. The thermos flask shows how insulation can be done really effectively.

The stopper is made from a **poor conductor** e.g. cork or plastic

The inner container is made of shiny glass to reduce **radiation**

Think carefully about each of the labels on the thermos flask.

The vacuum reduces the amount of energy that can be lost by **convection**

Try to link each of them to heat loss from your house

The plastic cover protects the glass inside

This space could be filled with sponge. The little bubbles would trap air and so reduce losses due to **convection**

the meaning of energy efficiency and the need for economical use of energy resources;

Using energy sensibly

Keeping the heating bills down (and doing the environment a favour at the same time) can be achieved in many ways.
The easiest way is to wear a few more clothes and then turn down the heating a bit.
There are also lots of things that we can do to our houses to make them better insulated.

Never mind what we look like, think of all the money we're saving on central heating.

Another of Mum's brilliant ideas!

The conservation of energy

Petrol

30% transferred

Chemicals

Motion and heat

85% transferred

Electricity

"Whirrr!"
10% transferred

Light and heat

Keeping the accounts

Let's follow 100 units of energy from petrol to light. Only 30 of those units appear as motion in the generator. 85% of this (25.5 units) appears as electricity. 10% (2.55 units) of this appears as light.
We conclude that petrol motors and filament light bulbs are not very efficient.
Only 2.55 units of the original 100 have appeared in the form we want (light). The rest is now in the form of heat, noise and unburnt fuel (smoke).

Entropy

There is a tendency for energy to spread out evenly amongst objects and therefore be less available for us to use (this isn't a definition of entropy by the way, the even spreading out is a result of entropy).

The energy in the flames here will not have gone when the fire goes out. It is still around, spread through the air above the fire, getting more spread out as time passes and therefore getting less useful to us.

---

work, power and energy

Forces, movement and work

A force is a push or a pull (measured in newtons).

Energy is transferred when a force moves an object. We call this energy transfer **'Work'**.

Work = Force x Distance moved
joules (J)   newtons (N)   metres (m)

Topic flow

Force & work
↓
power
↓
KE, PE & work
↓
efficiency

Mouse is calculating her maximum power by carrying a known weight up a known height in a known time.

She knows that this is definitely her maximum power and that she could not keep up that rate of work for an 8 hour day.

'Gasp !'
Heavy
'tick' 'tock'
'Wobble'
0.5 m

		units:
Work	work done = force x distance	joules (newton metres)
Power	power = $\dfrac{\text{work done}}{\text{time taken}}$	watts (joules per second)

Human Power (Average adult)			
Max power (for a few seconds)	1500 W	Sustained power (For an 8 hour day)	60 W

Potential energy

Potential energy is energy in a form that can be used when required. It is a store of energy such as there is in firewood, or in a full hydroelectric dam.

Kinetic energy

'Kinetic' means 'motion' and so kinetic energy involves things in motion . . . our bodies falling off a cliff, electrons drifting their way around a circuit, vibrating atoms and molecules in a flame.

$$KE = \frac{1}{2} mv^2$$

K. S. 4 Physical Processes	Energy resources and energy transfer

energy transfer

> If I carry a glass of milk up the stairs, the useful work has been done on the glass of milk. My body has also been taken upstairs and so the total work is much greater than the useful work.

Useful work and efficiency

Weight of glass of milk: 4 N
Weight of Benjie : 35 N
Height of stairs: 3 m

Useful work = 4 x 3
= 12 J
Total work = 39 x 3
= 117 J

$$\text{Efficiency} = \frac{\text{energy transferred as desired}}{\text{total energy transferred}} \times 100$$

$$= \frac{12}{117} \times 100$$

$$= 10\%$$

$$\text{Efficiency} = \frac{\text{work out}}{\text{work in}} \times 100 \qquad \text{Efficiency} = \frac{\text{energy out}}{\text{energy in}} \times 100$$

$$\text{Efficiency} = \frac{\text{power out}}{\text{power in}} \times 100$$

Efficiency is **always** less than 1 (or less than 100%)

> Here are another three forms of the equation that you might come across

---

radioactivity and the chain reaction

> that radioactivity arises from the breakdown of an unstable nucleus;

1. The uranium–235 atom is unstable and can disintegrate at any time, releasing 3 neutrons and some energy.
2. The atom will also disintegrate if it is hit by a neutron. When a uranium–235 atom disintegrates deep inside a large lump of uranium, the 3 neutrons are very likely to collide with 3 other atoms before they can escape from the lump.
3. The 3 atoms then disintegrate and release 9 neutrons which collide with more atoms so that up to 27 neutrons are released and so on !
4. All this happens within millionths of a second so that , in a flash, most uranium atoms disintegrate almost instantly, releasing huge amounts of energy.

> that there is background radioactivity;

Background radiation

As I sit here typing, radiation from the rocks below and from outer space is bombarding my body. In Norfolk, each thumb-sized volume in the body gets about 20 impacts per minute. We have a 60 m layer of non-radioactive chalk separating the humans from the bedrock and so the background is fairly low. Where the bedrock is closer to the surface, the radiation is more intense (particularly in granite-rich areas like Cornwall or Aberdeen) and may reach 40 impacts per second per thumb-sized volume.
Organisms have been surviving this level of radiation since life began and so you don't need to worry yourself about normal background radiation. We do need to worry about the levels of radon gas inside well-insulated houses though (radon gas leaks into houses from the soil).

> Mmmm background radiation. Let's see . . .

Walrus
guides for the discerning

| radioactivity | that there are three main types of radioactive emission with different penetrating powers; | the nature of alpha and beta particles and of gamma radiation; |

Types of radiation

Alpha (∝) particles

Alpha particles only travel a few centimetres in air; they are stopped by a sheet of paper. They change direction when passing through magnetic fields or when passing between charged plates. They seem to be the same as fast-moving helium atoms that have lost both their electrons. Because they are much more massive than Beta particles, they deviate less when passing through any particular field. Plutonium and Americium are almost pure Alpha sources. Alpha particles produce intense ionisation of the molecules in the air along their path.

Beta (ß) particles

Beta particles are fast-moving electrons. They are a bit more zippy than alpha particles, and travel several metres in air or through a few millimetres of aluminium. They are negatively charged and travel very fast (up to 90% of the speed of light).

They move in the opposite direction to ∝ particles when they pass through electric and magnetic fields.

I suggest that you make out your own summary table listing the important differences between the three types of radiation; alpha, beta and gamma (you could include X-rays and cosmic rays).

Gamma (γ) radiation

Gamma rays are not like Beta or Alpha particles. They are not affected by electric or magnetic fields. They travel at the speed of light and can pass through several centimetres of lead. They are very short wavelength, electromagnetic radiation. Cobalt 60 emits beta and gamma rays (the beta particles can be absorbed by several mm. of aluminium, leaving pure gamma rays).

X-rays and gamma rays

The main difference between gamma rays and X-rays is that gamma rays are given off when there are energy changes in the nucleus of the atom, whereas X-rays are given off because of changes in the electron arrangement of the atom outside the nucleus.

Half-life

Half-life is the time taken for the radioactivity of a substance to decay to half its original level. In one half-life, half of the original nuclei will disintegrate and form new (different) nuclei. Half-lives vary from a millionth of a second to millions of years. But it is always the same for the same isotope.

the meaning of the term 'half-life';

Element	Half-life
^{9}Lithium	0.17 sec.
^{38}Potassium	7.7 min.
^{55}Iron	2.7 yrs.
^{14}Carbon	5 570 yrs.
^{235}Uranium	4 500 000 yrs.

Notice the jagged line; that's because radiation is emitted in a fairly random sort of way.

Graph showing how activity decreases as time passes

Activity (arbitrary units)

background rate

See the next page for details on how to calculate the half-life from the graph

Time (seconds)

50   100   150   200   250

K. S. 4 Physical Processes | **Radioactivity**

Calculating the half-life

1. Draw a line of best fit through the jagged graph and then mark in the background rate.
2. Draw a horizontal line through a point on the graph at which the activity was fairly high.
3. Draw another horizontal line halfway between the two that you have already drawn.
4. Add a few more horizontal lines, each time halving the distance between the last line and the background rate.
5. Drop perpendiculars from the intersect of each horizontal line with the graph.
6. By now your graph should look like the one above (or on the right). The half-life is the average distance between the vertical lines (as read off the x axis scale)

The half-life shown on the last page is about 50 seconds

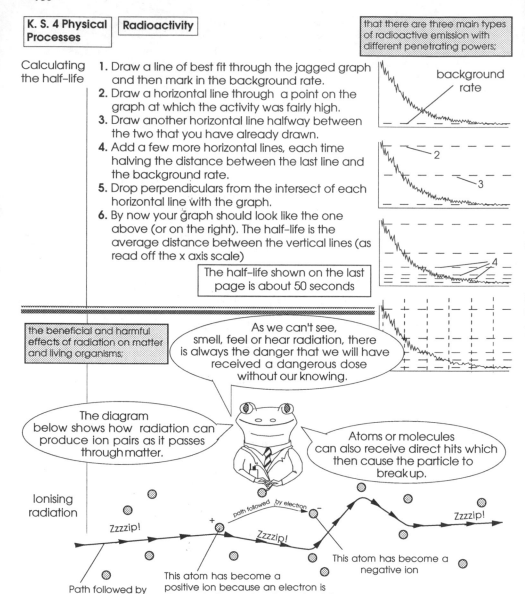

As we can't see, smell, feel or hear radiation, there is always the danger that we will have received a dangerous dose without our knowing.

The diagram below shows how radiation can produce ion pairs as it passes through matter.

Atoms or molecules can also receive direct hits which then cause the particle to break up.

Ionising radiation

Zzzzip!

path followed by electron

Zzzzip!

Zzzzip!

Path followed by the alpha particle

This atom has become a positive ion because an electron is dragged off one atom (or molecule) and settles on another.

This atom has become a negative ion

The dangers of radiation

We should keep the amount of radioactivity that hits our bodies to an absolute minimum! Ideally, this minimum should be only background radiation and radiation for essential medical uses (X-rays etc.).

Whenever radiation passes through our bodies, trails of ions are left in its wake. These ions (with their strong positive or negative charges) cause a great deal of local damage to molecules around them. Cells can be killed and mutations to the genetic material can occur.

Precautions — **There are certain precautions that should be taken by anyone likely to be exposed to radiation.**

1 Keep exposure (through X-rays or other treatments) to an absolute minimum.
2 Wear lead protection over the gamete-producing organs (ovaries or testicles) whenever this is possible (Damage to our own bodies is bad; damage to the next generation is worse).
3 If your work involves dealing with radiation, make sure you always wear the dosage monitor.
4 Never eat or smoke when working with radioactive materials (as it has been suggested that a third of all premature deaths are smoking related, you should probably not be smoking anyway).

You don't need to learn this detail, I put it in as I thought you might find it interesting. →

Dosage (RADs)	Death within	Symptoms
above 10^9	1 day	Vomiting, diarrhoea, convulsions, brain damage, coma.
10^8 to 10^9	2 weeks	Gut lining not replaced, inability to digest food, vomiting, diarrhoea, emaciation.
10^7	3-4 weeks	Blood cells not replaced, anaemia, fever, vomiting, bleeding, loss of hair.
$<10^7$	unknown	Inability to make antibodies, small wounds remain septic for long periods.

RAD — A person has received 1 RAD (dose of absorbed radiation) if each gram of their tissue has had a hundred thousandth of a joule of energy released in it (0.01 J per kg). This doesn't sound like very much, but it causes big problems because the energy is so concentrated. An air rifle pellet does not have very much energy but that does not stop it from damaging your calf muscle (it will go 6 or more centimetres deep).

Gray — A dose of 1 gray, means that 1 joule of energy has been absorbed by each kg of body tissue.

Sievert — The sievert is a measure of the biological effect of radiation.
No. of sieverts = Dose in grays x Q
(Q is a quality factor, i.e. how dangerous it is).

What can radioactivity be used for? — Radiation is **most damaging to cells which are busy dividing**. So, when any of us is subjected to radiation, tissues like **skin, intestine lining, hair, embryos** and **bone marrow cells** (where blood is being formed) show the effects first.

some uses of radioactivity, including the radioactive dating of rocks.

Cancer cells are constantly dividing and so are more susceptible to radiation damage than the surrounding tissue. For this reason, we can use radiation as a treatment for cancers.

Have another look at the table above and try to see the link between this paragraph and the table of symptoms.

The radiation treatment is combined with chemical treatment (chemotherapy), and the package can produce very unpleasant side-effects in the patient.

Patients may be prepared to put up with these side –effects if there is a good chance of curing the cancer. Some patients, with cancers that are difficult to cure, may make the brave decision that the quality of their last bit of life is more important than just being alive, and so may opt not to have the treatment (with all its nasty side–effects).

More on uses

Radioactive isotopes can also be used to:

1.   Kill bacteria in packaged food. Food sterilised in this way will keep 'fresh' for hundreds of years. (The radiation that kills the bacteria will also change the food molecules in small ways and could produce small amounts of nasty substances. It is for this reason that there has been quite a lot of opposition to the government legislation which allows radiated food to be made available to the public in the U.K.)

2.   Kill bacteria in medical materials like syringes, bandages, dressings and drip solutions.

3.   Check the thickness of paper during manufacture. This information is then fed back to the paper-making machine allowing it to adjust the paper thickness within very narrow limits (β radiation is used for this)

4.   Label, and then track, pollutants in rivers so that effective control measures can be taken.   By using isotopes with a short half-life for this work, radiation danger to the public is very slight.

5.   Detect whether certain parts of the human body are functioning as they should be (e.g. radioactive iodine is used to check thyroid gland function).

Dating organic remains and rocks using half lives

The basis of radioactive dating is that there is decay of an element to a daughter element which allows us to compare the concentration of each. The more daughter element in proportion to parent element the older the sample.

Natural carbon consists mainly of ^{12}C with a small amount of radioactive ^{14}C. The radioactive carbon is constantly being made in the upper atmosphere. This mixture of two carbons is taken up by plants as CO_2 when they photosynthesise and becomes part of their structure. When the plant dies ^{14}C is no longer taken up and the amount of ^{14}C steadily decreases due to radioactive decay.

By measuring the proportions of radioactive element to their daughter elements we can get quite a good idea of the age of organic remains up to about 10 000 years.

A table showing the parent and daughter elements and their half-lives	
Element pairs	half-life
Carbon^{14} - nitrogen	5570 million years
Uranium^{238} - lead	4497 million years
Uranium^{235} - lead	713 million years
Potassium^{40} - argon	11850 million years

By measuring the proportions of uranium and lead or of potassium and argon in a rock sample it is possible to get an idea of how long the radioactive decay has been in progress i.e. it is possible to get an idea of how long ago the rock was formed.

Index

Index

Index

Some rules for writing S I units

1. A full stop is not needed after a unit except at the end of a sentence.
2. There is no plural form of a unit; e.g. 40 N, 70 kg.
3. Only the units named after famous scientists have capital initial letters; e.g. watts (W), newtons (N).

Physical quantity	Name of the S I unit		Given as S I units	Useful equations
length	metre	m		
Mass	kilogram	kg		
time	second	s		
electric current	ampere	A		$I = \dfrac{Q}{t}$
temperature	kelvin	K		
amount of substance	mole	mol		
work (energy transfer)	joule	J	$kg\,m^2s^{-2}$	work = force x distance
force	newton	N	$kg\,m\,s^{-2}$	force = mass x acceleration
power	watt	W	$J\,s^{-1}$	$P = \dfrac{Work\ done}{time}$
speed			$m\,s^{-1}$	$speed = \dfrac{distance}{time}$